Dreams of Prophecies

Dreams of Prophecies

JOYCE TORRI

To order additional copies of this book, contact:
Xlibris Corporation
1-888-795-4274
www.Xlibris.com
Orders@Xlibris.com
28447

Contents

PART I

Credibility

PART II

Dreams of Prophecies

PART III

The Quest for Safety

Dedication

I have known Laverne Anderson for fourteen years. We became acquainted when I went to her as a client. From the first moment I laid eyes upon her, I knew that in some way we were connected; together, we shared a destiny. We have been sisters in past lives. In this life, we are soul sisters. She is my loyal friend and confidant. I consider her my rock to lean on.

I have told her about my prophecy dreams from the very beginning. Each time I've explained one of the dreams to her, she, in matter of seconds, has found the prophecy in the Bible and quoted it to me. She has been most helpful to me throughout this entire book of dreams. Laverne, my spiritual sister completely understands my dreams, their meanings and me. Whenever I've needed comforting, she has set my fears aside.

My soul has been enlightened with the beauty of hers, over a thousand times. Laverne's entire being is filled with kindness and love. I can't thank God enough for allowing our pathways to cross during this lifetime. The love I have for this woman will never die. I dedicate "Dreams of Prophecies" to her.

1996 Joyce Torri

"He who has ears to hear, let him hear."
Matthew 11:15

My heartfelt thanks to

Jim Brown,
who re-entered my life at precisely the right time,
giving me the boost I needed to get the book on it's way
and helped me with the hard work of it's first stages.

My sister Ev, who gave me her loyal support all of the
way. I would also like to thank Ginny Fauvelle, Tina
O'Banion, Betty Hofer, Chris Curtis and all of my
"readies" that are anxiously awaiting the publication.

My Underwriter

Gina O'Banion
A gift from God

*I*n the beginning Gina came to me as a client. Over the following months, she became like a daughter to me. She, a young woman of just eighteen was spiritually interested in my book and wanted to help me get it on the market.

Gina came to me inexperienced. However, during the months she worked for me she became a very good underwriter. It is not often that you will find an underwriter as young as Gina, who seemed to just know from the very beginning how I wanted it to be written. God sent her to me.

I owe her my deepest gratitude for staying until the very end; nearly a decade later, completing the book with me. She has most certainly found a place in my heart, for all lifetimes to come.

Foreword

This Book Belongs To God

*1*993 was my year of three; the smaller number of my birth sign. The larger number of my birth sign, four is what controlled my happenings.

In July of 1993 the inside of my house caught fire. I lost almost everything I had inside of the house due to smoke damage and the toxic fumes of chemicals. My thirteen-year-old calico cat, Colli and Cyndi, my Lhasa Apso dog were trapped inside and died from smoke inhalation.

In November of 1993 I became extremely ill. I was so close to death, I saw my great grandmother and mother waiting for at the foot of my bed. I knew that I was dying and I felt myself slip into the darkness. I saw the golden light. The light, which so many people have spoken of, does indeed exist. I awoke to find myself still among the living. I was very angry that God had not taken me and I became very depressed.

When I returned home the inside of my house had been remodeled. I filled the new interior of my home with my most treasured items, which were amazingly returned to me unharmed. I was so grateful to find my crystal and other antiques in one piece. As I unwrapped each plate I began crying. This is when I recovered my faith in God. In one breath, I thanked Him for returning all of my most treasured possessions to me. They were all as good as new.

From that day forward, I knew that God had sent me back to this world for a reason. There was a purpose for my existence. I decided to take each day as it came to me. Three months later my health had essentially improved. This is when the prophecy dreams began coming to me. As God sent them to me I wrote them down on paper, one by one, exactly as they had occurred in the dream. My Bible, along with all of my other books was lost in the fire so each time I had a dream I called Laverne. She read the scriptures for each of the dreams to me over the phone. I was simply amazed to hear the similarities between the scripture and the dream.

I believe that God sent me the dreams to enable the writing of this book. His purpose for this book is to inform the world of what is to come in a way that everyone is capable of understanding. This is why my dreams came in the form of stories.

This book is His, from beginning to end. I've only been His servant, my pen in my hand. Honor has filled my heart because He chose me as a prophet. I was chosen to send His messages out amongst all of you who purchase and read the book.

I ask each of you to open the door, embrace the light and let your life flow as a river; these things will lead you to the Lord, Our God.

Introduction

Dreams and prophecies have been a basic part of my entire life. Through periods of my life, these dreams and prophecies have been long and far in coming. However, when they do arrive, I dream in vivid color. Everything that I have dreamed of, in this way, has eventually made its presence into my life.

These dreams present themselves to me in a way that is equivalent to a story unfolding into a written book. In my dreams, I see everything, including the most trivial details. My dreams can expand over very long periods of time. Sometimes, I will dream of one thing for a few nights and then, the dream can disappear for several weeks or months. When the dream returns, it manifests from the last thing I envisioned. Eventually, each dream comes to a definite ending.

Numerology and astrology govern everything in our lives. Together, overruling you from the time you are born until the hour you passover in death and even, thereafter . . .

PART I

Credibility

A Client's Test

As a child, my psychic ability was tested. Sometimes the tests were almost beyond endurance. My family did not want me to be the way I am and they fought against it with every inch of energy they could muster. Back then; everyone accused me of being totally different. As I grew older this did not change. People referred to me as the ice maiden or as the girl that never seems to be here. I was told that my eyes were strange, that they looked like glass. Actually the last statement holds a bit of truth because as I go deeper into the psychic world my eyes do become a deeper shade of blackish blue. They become almost like a looking glass that actually can take you back into past lives. Sometimes, this happens without the person even realizing what is going on and where they are.

One of the reasons I chose to read cards was to distract people from looking into my eyes. I've never needed anything to read a person. By hearing a person's voice I know exactly where they are and who they are. I know even if the person is speaking to me on a phone from thousands of miles away. During the time I lived in Reno I began doing readings for people all around the world. Everything I have told people in my readings has come true but doing so many readings was wearing me to a frazzle. I wasn't able to get the proper amount of sleep and I didn't even have time to eat. All in all, I felt that it was unworthy of my time so I stopped doing the readings for everyone. From that day forward, the only readings I do are those recommended by word of mouth and to this day; no one enters my home without a recommendation.

I clearly remember the first evening I met a client by the name of Betty. From the moment she entered my trailer she began making remarks like: So how good are you? Really just how good are you? And, I've heard you're psychic, why don't you tell me something about myself? I asked myself, "Joyce, why are you allowing yourself to be tested like this by a woman whose sight you can't stand?" How dare somebody come into my home and doubt my abilities but she had and I began her reading.

When I finished the reading she said, "Well, you seem to be okay with your readings. I suppose we'll just have to wait to see if the things you've said come true or not. Nothing I've been told by any of the previous psychics I've seen has happened." I looked at Betty, who was a complete stranger to me that evening, straight in the eyes as I said, "I guarantee you Betty, what I say is going to happen. You can take that to the bank." She challenged me again by saying, "What makes you think you're that good? Why don't you tell me what has happened to me during my life? Then, I'll know if you're as good as you claim to be or not."

I was outraged by what I had just heard. I looked her in the eyes and said, "You have two children, and you did have three." There were tears in her eyes when she replied, "If I had three children and now I have only two then what happened to the one that is not here, that you didn't see?" I said, "Do you really want me to continue with this?" She looked at me in a very matter of fact way, straight in the eyes and said, "Yes, I do." I clearly saw what had happened to her eldest daughter and I asked her if she truly wanted me to continue. She answered, "I've got to know if you're good, go ahead and say it." So I did. "Your older daughter and another girl were killed. They were taken to the top of a hill and that is where they were murdered." Betty looked at me and said, "How were they murdered? Which one was killed first?" I looked back at her eyes and told her that they had been shot with a gun. Tears were streaming down her face when she said, "Please stop. I've heard everything I need to hear."

I stopped. I sat down and closely observed this lady. After a minute or so, I said, "It would be wise for you to never, ever again, test me because I will dig up things that no one but you knows of."

After her first reading, Betty frequently came back to my trailer. As the years passed we became best friends. Betty was even my roommate for more than a decade.

I've been tested by many of the people who have come to me for readings. Some have left my house crying while others have left irate, swearing, in a state of denial, that what I've told them was never going to happen. Some of them have actually come back to my house to tell me that what I said had indeed happened.

Letter From A Client

To: Joyce
From: Kathy Brown – Seattle, Wash.

I have had Joyce read my cards for approximately 7-8 years and find her accurate.

I'll never forget a reading she did for me on 4-6-93. She had said that you will soon hear of an accident near water due to illness or an accident. Then, she said, "This involves a fair haired man – light eyes and hair. He will die. And, a lady mourning."

I got home that week and received a letter from one of my best friends in Michigan. Her house caught fire on exactly 4-6-93 at 6am local time Michigan. Her boyfriend of 8 years, Tom died just before Easter from burns over 90% of his body. I flew down to be with her & their little boy Kyle. This was very accurate of Joyce – How she picked up on this.

There have been many other readings she has been most accurate. I have friends that continue to go to her and she is the "Best" "Gifted" person we go to: and will continue to go to.

Sincerely,
Kathy Brown

One Who Felt Her Life Was Hopeless

I do not wish to reveal this client's name so she will be referred to as Anne.

*F*our years ago I did a reading for a woman by the name of Anne. Although she had been a client of mine for a few years, I had no idea how extremely depressed she'd become after losing her job as an interior decorator. Anne had not been able to find another job and was very concerned about her finances. I did a reading for her and before she left I said, "Do not worry about this because God has a direction for you to go in. You will reach it in time." Anne replied, "It's a good thing I believe in you." I felt a tremendous burden had been placed on my shoulders by her last remark because I knew that she might take her life if anything I told her was wrong.

Six months had passed and there was not a job to be had in this town. Anne had lost her unemployment benefits and therefore, lost her apartment. She moved in with a friend, put most of her belongings in a storage unit and continued searching for work. She lived with her friend for five months and then moved in with one of her girlfriends.

Anne came to see me and explained everything that had happened. She was in a much deeper state of depression and this frightened me tremendously. She said, "Now, I've lost all of the things, including my furniture that were in storage because I couldn't pay the unit's rent. I just feel like there is nothing left. I feel like my life is over." That day, I flat out said, "The material possessions are not important. Anne, you cannot take them with you. You need to be free in order to go toward your destination. You need to be able to pack your bag and be own your way."

She had been living with her girlfriend for two months but her girlfriend had met a man and he was going to move in. Because of this, Anne moved in with her son. She would stay with one friend and then with another but knew things couldn't continue the way they were for much longer.

Finally, Anne came to me more depressed and desperate than she'd ever been. I told her that she'd receive an offer from Los Angeles within two weeks. I said, "You will not get this job but I want you to go there even if you have to hawk your shoes to get there because it will be the most important change you will have in your entire life." She looked at me and said, "How can it be when I've already lost everything? I don't even care for life anymore." I looked back at her with a stern face and replied, "You must go. They will not accept you at the interview but you will have lunch with them. They will tell you that you are not qualified before the end of the day, nevertheless, you must go."

Her son gave her the money she needed for the plane fare. She went to the interview, had lunch and was informed that she did not have the qualifications the company was looking for. Anne went straight to the airport to wait for her flight because she was a stand-by passenger. The flight had been overbooked. The stewardess told Anne she would have to wait for the next flight, which was scheduled to take off at ten fifteen the next morning. Anne had only three dollars to her name and that was not enough for her to eat dinner. She was going to have to spend the night at the airport terminal and simply wait for her flight. She held back her tears as she turned away from the ticket counter. She was devastated. We've all felt like we've come to the last straw in our life and this was Anne's last straw. She held her head down as she walked away.

In the meantime, a businessman was standing at the ticket counter across the terminal from Anne. His flight to Germany had also been overbooked and he was going to have to wait for the next plane. He was walking down the terminal when Anne ran straight into him. She glanced up at the man and burst into tears. The man, startled by this, said, "Nothing could be that bad. We need to have a drink and get you straightened out. Maybe you can tell me about it." She shook her head yes and they walked around the corner to the airport bar. They ordered their drinks and began to talk. After a few hours, the man asked Anne if she would like to have dinner with him and she accepted.

The two had hit it off very well. Anne had needed someone other than her family and close friends to confide in. She felt she could confide in this man without completely giving herself away. They finished their dinner at around nine o'clock that evening. As they were preparing to leave the restaurant the man said, "May I have the courtesy of getting you a hotel room?" He explained that he also had to get a room and that both of the rooms would be charged on his account at no expense to him. He told her that he would like to have breakfast with her before she boarded her plane. She accepted his offer.

The next morning, which was Saturday morning, they ate an early breakfast. The man asked if she would stay for the rest of the weekend so they could get to know each other better. Once again she accepted his offer. By the end of the weekend, Anne discovered that she really liked this man and when he asked her if they could keep in touch, she gave him her home address.

The next day she received red roses from him. For the next two months they were in constant touch with each other. Each day, Anne received a long distance phone call, a letter or flowers. She loved the roses he sent and found herself looking forward to his phone calls. So, when he sent her a letter asking her to come to Germany for two months, she agreed.

Before leaving town, Anne came to me to get my thoughts on her trip. I told her that she would like the man but that she would hate the country. She would swear she would not return to Germany but she would.

Anne found that she felt isolated in Germany; that is other than the time she spent with the man whom she did adore. She hated the country mainly because she couldn't speak the language. Two months later, Anne returned to Reno and stayed at her parents' home. The man continued sending flowers and writing letters to her. A month later, he asked if he could visit her in America and she said yes.

The man stayed in Reno for a week. He asked Anne to return to Germany for three months to give the country another chance. After much deliberation on Anne's part, she decided to go with him. By the time he was ready to leave, her bags were packed.

Although she and this man were very much in love, she was out of her element. She felt that not being able to speak the German language was a great barrier to cross. She was not accustomed to their way of living, either. The apartment she was staying in did not have a refrigerator or a washing machine. During Anne's second stay, I received several long distance phone calls from her. I told her not to worry about the conditions they were living in because it would pass. They would wind up in a beautiful home of their own which she would love. Also, I prescribed herbs that cured her of diverticulitis.

The man suggested that Anne enroll in classes to learn to speak German. She did enroll and when she began to understand the language she found herself really enjoying life. The couple became caretakers of a very wealthy estate. The owners of the estate had not been there in over three years so basically they had the home to themselves.

Three years passed before they returned to the States. They were married at Lake Tahoe. Two days after their wedding, the couple came to see me. They brought their wedding pictures for me to see and I don't think I'd ever seen a happier person than Anne.

A year later she returned to Reno from Germany. Her parents were moving out of the area and she and her husband had come to help them move. They came to see me. Anne told me she would probably never return. She said to me, "I had to tell you that you have been the salvation of my life. Everything you foretold has happened and I truly didn't need any of the material possessions that were once held so dear to me. I have received more where I'm living now than I ever had before and I actually prefer the lifestyle in Germany." She went on to explain that it was more like the olden days in Germany and at slower pace.

Anne had never looked better. I hugged her and wished both of them well. Her destiny was not in America. It was in Germany with her husband. To my knowledge they are still happily living together.

The Client Who Refused To Believe

About three years ago, around the twenty-third or twenty-fourth of February I did a reading for a very attractive young lady. When I completed her reading the cards for her I told her something that had nothing to do with the cards.

I looked directly at her and said, "I want to warn you about what will be happening on the nineteenth or twentieth of August. You will be traveling to a campsite. You will have to drive on a dirt road. When you reach the dirt road I want you to roll up your window and fasten your seat belt because you are going to have an accident. If you do as I tell you to, you will not be harmed but the car is going to be totally destroyed." She said, "I don't think that is going to be the case at all, Joyce. Because, number one, I never go camping – I hate it and number two, I would never go down a dirt road in the summer. I hate the country and why I would ever be going there, I don't know." I said, "Okay, Cathy. But just remember, when you hit that dirt road you are going to hit a lot of sand. Roll up your window and fasten your seat belt."

Cathy left adamant that this was one thing I said that was not going to happen. With people who are positive what I say will not happen, often I just simply say what I have to say and dismiss it. They will have to find out themselves.

The following September, Cathy came back to me because she needed a reading. I asked her how she'd been because I had not seen her in several months. She said, "I have a confession to make to you. I think you ought to know that what you told me would happen, happened." Well, it had been seven or eight months since I'd seen this lady and I'd done hundreds of readings for other people so I said, "What was that, that I told you Cathy?" She replied, "I did indeed go on June the nineteenth to meet someone at a camp place. I turned off the road and hit the loose sand. Immediately, my mind triggered into action; I rolled up my window and fastened my seat belt. I traveled no more than twenty-five feet further down the road when deep ruts of sand pitched my car sideways and down a deep, very steep ravine. The car flipped over, twenty-five times. I was able to open my door and walk back up to the top of the hill. I looked down at my car and saw that it was totally destroyed. I don't know how you knew but I know one thing, you saved my life." I gave her a smile and said, "This is why God gave me the gift Cathy; to help save lives, bring people peace of mind by letting them know there is a future, a destiny for all of us. That by trusting in God you will be delivered to these things."

Identifying Illnesses

D ancing has always been a form of therapy for me. Over the years, I've had many male friends that have been very good dance partners. One these friends was a man by the name of Jim. He is an excellent dancer and we've danced together for many years.

As he dropped me off at home after a night of dancing he asked if I would do a reading on him. I said that I would and he followed me inside. As I read him I continually picked up on something going wrong with his knee. When I told him about this he replied, "There's nothing wrong with my knee. And, there better not be because I ski." I repeated my warning to watch out for his knee and left it at that.

One month later, I ran into him while I was out and about running errands. He told me that something had indeed gone wrong with his knee and that he could no longer dance or ski because of it. He asked me how I knew. I replied, "Well, I'm one in a million that can find illnesses in people. Even those illnesses that the doctors can't seem to identify."

In the month of February a similar thing happened. A professional man (whose name I will not mention) came to see me as one of my clients. While doing a reading on him I knew that he would be having prostate problems. I point blank asked him about this. He told me he had just had a complete physical and was perfectly healthy. I informed him that on the nineteenth of June he would be having prostrate surgery. He looked at me with total disbelief.

Nine months later, he came back to me. He had, in fact, had surgery on his prostate on the exact day I said he would – the ninethenth of June.

I had known a man by the name of Bill for about three months. We did not have a serious relationship but each time he flew in to Reno from Las Vegas we went out together. Usually we each brought a friend and the four of us went out to dinner. While we dined, we discussed the psychic world among many other things and when we were through with our meal we would go dancing.

One night while we were dancing together he said, "Joyce with your psychic abilities can you pick up on a person's health?" I answered, "Yes I have a basic overview. Bill, you seem to be in pretty good shape but you are too thin. I think the reason for this is being caused by something in your brain." He jokingly asked me if I was trying to tell him that he was crazy. I said to him, "No. I'm trying to tell you that within three months you will not be able to work in your office because you will have such violent headaches. The first time one of these headaches occur, please go to your doctor and have it checked out."

After we had this conversation, I did not see or hear from Bill for three months. And then I received a phone call from him. He apologized for not returning to Reno and for not staying in contact with me. Bill told me that he had not been feeling very well. He said, "I've been having extremely violent headaches and none of the doctors have been able to figure out what is wrong with me."

A week or two after the phone call he flew into Reno. Bill and I made dinner plans and agreed that just the two of us would go this time. I picked him up from the hotel he was staying at and we went out for dinner. By this time, he was really not feeling well and we both felt it was best to not go dancing after we finished eating. It was late in the summer and as I drove him back to the hotel, the sun was still shining. We said goodnight to each other. As I drove off he stood on the corner waving good-bye. I suddenly realized what I was seeing wave to me was an actual skeleton, not Bill. I knew, then and there, that I would never see this man again; he was going to die.

Late in the evening about two months later, he called me. He explained to me that the doctors had found a cancerous tumor in his brain and that he was going down to Mexico to have it operated on by a psychic surgeon. Bill wanted me to accompany him on the trip. I told him that I wasn't able to go because I couldn't get the time off from work but I would be there in spirit and soul. I also told him to call me just before he went into surgery.

He went to Mexico for the operation and the surgeon was able to remove a great deal of the cancerous tumor. However, four months later, in spite of all efforts, I was informed by one of his friends (who lived in Reno) that Bill had passed away. From that point on, I am thoroughly convinced that if I see a skull instead of a body, that person is on their way out of this world and into a new life.

Finding Objects, Animals And People

T hroughout the course of my life, I have found wallets, jewelry, children and dogs. I have even told the police about murders, and described murder victims only to be shunned.

In this instance, I was able to ease a mother's mind.

About twelve years ago, Carol and I had just become friends. She called me one morning and told me she felt something was going on with her twelve-year-old son. I told her to call me in the afternoon if she still thought something was wrong.

I received a second phone call from Carol that afternoon. She informed me that her boy had not come home after school. He had not even gone to school according to his teacher. The boy had threatened her, when he was angry, that he was going to leave town on a freight train. She was positive that he and another boy had done this. In my mind, I clearly saw what the boys had done. I said, "The two boys did not get on a freight train." I told her that I felt they were still in town. She said, "But how are they going to eat? They don't have any money." I told her that I saw some loose change in their pockets and that they manage. She said, "But where on earth will they sleep?"

A vision of an old, abandoned filling station with an attached garage came to me. It was located on the outer edge of the city of Sparks. The building had not been used for a long time. Inside the building, there were rusty cans and things leftover from when the station was abandoned. I also saw an old mattress. Children would sleep for part of the day and then a man would find them. He was a caretaker and would make them move out of the garage. They would wander around until dark. They would sleep in a large park with a lot of trees, big trees hanging overhead. They would be cold, tired and hungry. She was concerned about the chill of the night but it was still summer and I said that the children would be all right. I said, "By the morning, they will have learned their lesson. They will return home before ten."

Carol called me the following evening. She said, "What you said is exactly what happened. They did find the old station, slept on the mattress, were ordered to leave and wound up sleeping in the park. They returned because they were cold and hungry."

Tuning into the
Mind of an Animal

I received a phone call from a regular client of mine's friend. This friend, who we'll call John, was calling only two days after I'd done a reading for the client. He was calling for the woman because she was quite upset, as her large dog had somehow gotten out of her apartment. He said, "She's fallen all to pieces. The dog has never been out of an apartment and now he's lost. Do you know where the dog is at?" I replied, "Go down the streets near the apartment. Go two streets in one direction and two streets in the other. There will be a house with a white picket fence on the left hand side. The dog did not stay there however, the woman at the house may be able to tell you what direction he went in." Bill, my friend who had come by to visit, was listening from the rocking chair on the patio and heard the telephone conversation from beginning to end.

This woman had been quite depressed for sometime; worried, as I believe most of us are, about what tomorrow may bring. I thought she was a pretty terrific woman who had just had some hard things come down on her lately. When I'd done her reading, I straight out told her that her heart was going to be tried by pain. She believed it would be concerning her job but I told her that I didn't think that was it.

John called me the following afternoon. He told me that he had found the house with the white picket fence. It was on the left hand side of the street and a woman was there. The woman told John that she had seen the dog but didn't stop him because she had a dog herself. John called again the next afternoon. He said, "She's hysterical and very, very depressed." Her heart was being tried by pain; she was grieving for her dog. I had a deep feeling that if her dog made it to the freeway he would be killed.

You've probably heard of or seen how the power of the mind works either from books, movies or television. In my years, I've told many people if their animals were dead or alive. If the animal was alive I've told the owner around what element they would find their pet. With the power of my mind I can reach animals. I can make them hear me and obey my commands. That evening I began to meditate. I told the missing dog to turn around and go home. I meditated to the dog during every spare moment I had and once before I went to bed. I knew that for a short period of time, the dog had taken up with a black and white spotted dog. I also knew that when they separated the dog would still be lost but that I could get him to turn around and go home.

Again, I received a phone call from John. He said, "The dog has been missing for three days. We don't know where to look. We've searched six blocks in every direction." I sensed that the dog was very close to the freeway. I told the man to start traveling the streets. It was essentially important the he begin now and go down the street that was nearest the freeway. I gave him the name of the street and told him that this would be where he could locate the dog. In the meantime, I connected my mind with the dog's. I put a shield of protection around him and told him to follow his instinct and travel in the direction he had come from.

A couple of hours later John called me back. He said, "I found the dog a few yards from the freeway on the street you told me I would. Ironically, it looked like he was trying to head home." He told me that I had restored his faith in God and thanked me. John called to thank me again the next day. He told me that he truly appreciated the gift that I had and that someday he would come to see me.

The Spiritual Blue Light

T hree weeks before my son Casey was to graduate from Loyalton High School he came to see me at my trailer at Bonanza Square. He needed some money so I wrote a check out and gave it to him. When Casey was ready to leave I walked with him down the hill to where he'd parked his pick-up truck. I gave him a hug good-bye and stood aside as he got into his truck and started the motor. Casey put the truck in reverse and began backing up. As he did, I saw a vision of his truck tumbling over and over down a steep ravine located close to Sierraville. My vision was startling and I was shocked. I grabbed my neck with both hands. I knew then and there that my son's neck would soon be broken.

I was sobbing so hard as I went up the stairs to my porch that I stumbled and badly bruised my leg. I was so upset by my vision that my leg just didn't matter. I fell on my knees to the floor in the living room and continued to cry my heart out. Betty had come to visit me from Carson City. When she saw me crying she asked me what on earth had happened. I explained the vision of my son to her. When I was finished she raised herself out of the chair and kneeled beside me on the floor. Betty said, "Surely you can do something to stop this from happening." Between my sobs, I managed to tell her that it was a destiny for the pick-up truck to flip over the canyon. The truck would roll seventy-five feet before it stopped.

I silently sat on the floor for several minutes as I prayed for God to help me protect my son. Then, the blue light began to shimmer in front of me. I knew it was impossible to stop the truck from falling down the ravine however; I could protect my son when it happened. I placed a blue shield of light around his neck and reinforced the seat belt so that he would be held in his seat as the truck rolled over and over, down the steep canyon.

Three weeks later, my son and his girlfriend began driving to Truckee, California. It was the night of his graduation and they had just attended a party. Ten miles out of Sierraville my son lost control of his pick-up as he went around a sharp turn. The truck plummeted seventy-five feet down the cliff. The trunk of a tree braced it.

Casey's girlfriend was not injured. She hiked up the cliff and flagged down a car. She told the people what had happened and asked them to send an ambulance at once. Shortly thereafter, an ambulance arrived. It took the emergency team a considerable amount of time to hike down the hill and back up with my son on a stretcher. They believed his neck was broken.

My ex-husband was informed of the accident and he met the ambulance at the Loyalton Hospital. Casey's father was in the emergency room the entire time the doctor that was on duty examined our son. The doctor told my ex-husband, Ken that he could not get to Casey's neck. The doctor explained that something was around Casey's neck and it prevented him from examining it. The doctor said, "I don't know what it is but it has saved your son's life."

At around six o'clock in the morning I received a phone call from Ken. He explained what had happened to our son.

It was word for word as I'd seen in my vision. He said, "The strangest thing happened. Something invisible was around Casey's neck." Neither he nor the doctor knew what it was but whatever it was had saved Casey's life. I told my ex-husband that I had placed a band of blue light around our son's neck. To this day I don't think Ken has grasped the meaning of this. But, I certainly have and I immediately thanked God. My son had come out of the accident without a scratch. Casey walked out of the hospital with his father holding on to his arm.

I learned of the blue light thirty years ago when I attended classes on psychicness. A woman professor taught the classes from Berkeley College in California. Instead of using the training I received in the classes I became an artist. I sold fifteen years of paintings before I left my home in California. When I moved to Reno I began doing readings again. Between two jobs I no longer had time to paint landscapes. To this day, I only do paintings by special request.

I had a woman ask me if I had any religious beliefs. I told her that I was Catholic. Referring to my readings, she said, "Don't you know that the Catholic Church would frown upon you doing this?" I replied, "God gave me the gift of psychic abilities. I don't need cards to read you. I use the cards to keep people from staring into my eyes." My eyes become a bluish black and are very glassy when I read people. If a person stares into my eyes they transgress into other lifetimes. Some began to shake and a few have even passed out.

When the women left, I began to wonder about the church and my tarots. I put a blue shield around my four sets of cards and the desk drawer I kept them in. One of the sets of tarot cards was one hundred and fifty years old. They were given to me to carry on by a woman named Millie Voone. Another set of cards in the drawer I had had since the age of thirteen. I asked God to show me a sign, that if I was doing the wrong thing by helping people in this manner to let me know.

I am a great collector of antiques such as furniture, cut glass plates, cups and saucers. During one of my daughter's visits she noticed my newest collection item, an oblong dish with hand painted pansies. Susan told me that when I died the plate was hers and she asked me to make sure that the plate was hung securely on the dining room wall. I lifted my eyes to the plate. I protected the plate but did not bother with the other things on the wall – a small floral wreath and two collector plates with humming birds.

Seven days before the inside of my house burned, I mentioned to my roommate Betty that we needed new cabinets, new doors and I wished that I could put a skylight in the kitchen. Because of the fire, the inside of my house was completely remodeled within three months.

When I entered my home for the first time after the fire I had to wear a mask over my face because the toxic fumes were so strong. I walked straight over to my roll top desk, which was set in the dining room. I opened it and found that some of the keys on my word processor were melted. My gold jewelry that had been locked inside of the bottom drawer was also melted. Next, I opened the drawer my cards were inside of. I pulled out the drawer and was simply amazed. All four sets of cards were just as I had left them. They were in perfect condition, even the ones that were hand painted.

I thanked God that my house had been saved; that not everything had been completely destroyed. I also thanked Him for giving me my tarot cards. I knew that because they didn't even have a trace of smoke damage that He wanted me to continue helping people in the manner I had been.

I glanced over to the wall where the plate with the pansies hung. I fully expected to see it shattered like most of my other antiques. The wallpaper had been burned off of the wall, the wreath was burned and my two humming bird plates were shattered into a million pieces on the floor. The only thing that remained on the wall was the plate with the pansies. When I removed it from the wall, the wallpaper behind it was in perfect condition.

I had protected the outside of my house with the blue light but I had not thought of protecting the inside. The fire was put out before it reached the roof; only one rafter was scorched.

or

ers

ildren and my own were quite
young I was still living on the ranch. Usually, I
took care of all the children on the weekends. They had a
fabulous time as they literally ran wild. One evening I picked
up Denny to rock her in my old fashioned rocker. Denny
was my sister's oldest child and she loved being rocked in
my arms for a short period of time. The other children were
playing with one another at my feet. This was the perfect
time for me to spend with Denny before her father picked
her up the following afternoon.

As I held her in my arms, I visioned Denny never giving
birth to a child. I wondered why this was. She seemed to be
a very healthy child far healthier than either of my children
had ever thought of being. Yet, I could not shake this thought
from my mind. My heart was filled with dread as I thought
of this little girl's future.

At the age of nineteen, my niece was diagnosed with
cervical cancer. Her only option was a complete
hysterectomy. She was never able to have her own child
however she was able to compensate this loss. Denny moved
out of Reno and became a kindergarten teacher. She also

established a program that tests the abilities of disabled children. To this day, her work with children continues and she is doing quite well.

The second prediction came for my sister's second daughter, Coleen. When she was thirteen I knew that she would only have one child and that it would be a son. This meant that my sister would only have one grandchild. They were going to be very close to each other. My sister would be helping her daughter and grandson when they needed help the most. I saw the boy standing over the oven helping my sister bake cookies. I watched them remove the cookies from the oven.

Uncannily, on one of my sister's visits, she asked if I felt she was going to have any grandchildren. I told her that she would have one and it would be a boy. I told her that the father would not stay with the mother and that she would help support her daughter and grandson for a period of time. Her grandson would be very close to her throughout his entire childhood.

My niece's pregnancy seemed to swiftly pass by for everyone except her. When Coleen went into labor, my sister called to ask if I would comfort Coleen with the calmness of my voice. I told her I would be there soon. I quickly straightened up my trailer and got dressed. I arrived at the hospital early in the morning. After a few hours, my sister said, "Coleen is literally worn out. When do you think the baby will be born?" I replied, "The boy will be born at seven twenty-seven p.m."

As the baby was born, I watched from the corridor through the door that was ajar. I saw my sister standing on the right side of Coleen, near her head. On Coleen's left I saw her father. Her father had died of leukemia many years ago but he was watching as his grandson came into the world. The baby was named William. He was born at exactly twenty-seven minutes past seven o'clock that evening. William is a gifted and talented young man. As a teenager, he has had a poem, a children's book and an adult book published. Words flow from William like the stream of a river. He will go on to do many things. Most important of these things will be his spiritualness. He may even be psychic, in his latter years.

The third prediction came to me in the form of a dream. It was about my daughter, Susan who had recently graduated from Davis and joined the forest service. She was working in a remote area of Oregon.

In my dream, it had rained and there were muddy puddles everywhere. My daughter had just left a cattle ranch because she was with range cattle on the district grazing land. She was riding her horse on a dirt road. Her dog, Sam was at her side (as he always was) to protect Susan. She had raised Sam since he was a puppy and they were very close. When Sam's feet got sore from running he rode on her saddle.

The rancher, whom she had just left, was on a horse behind her. The man was chasing her with the intention of physically violating her. Susan would not bear this man molesting her. She was terrified and whipping her horse with all of her might. Sam was racing through the forest at her side. His ears were straight up in the air. Little streams and puddles covered the dirt road. This put Susan in more danger because the horse could easily slide or fall. In the end, Susan made it to a place with other people and was able to save herself from this destiny.

I didn't say a word about my dream to anyone because I thought if I put it into words it would surely happen. I spent several days worrying and fretting about the dream. I prayed for Susan to receive God's protection. I put a shield around her, hoping it would save her like it had once saved my son.

My daughter has been the biggest test of my entire life. Susan did not want her mother to be different in any way. She would work from dusk to dawn trying to prove that her mother was not psychic and that what I said would most assuredly never happen.

During a visit in my new house, Susan said, "I don't know how people put up with you Mother. How can they believe the stuff you say when half of it will never even be possible. You don't even know anything about me." I calmly turned around to look directly into Susan's eyes. I said, "I'm going to tell you about a dream I had. I hope that it hasn't already happened. If it hasn't, I want to warn you because it is coming. Never let a man follow you through the woods. And, never go down a dirt road alone after it has rained. Always make sure someone is with you." A stricken look appeared on her face. She said, "Mom, have you just told me about the future or the past?" I replied, "This danger I felt around you could've been in the recent past. If it has not happened, I guarantee you it will. Pay close attention to my dream." Susan cut me off when she softly whispered, "It already has happened. I barely got away. Could it happen again?" "Not if it has already happened," I said. "Remember to stay out of the woods when it rains and don't go down that road again." She closed the matter by nodding her head.

I believe I opened my daughter's eyes that day. I gained her respect because she had never told anyone what had happened. I wished that she had told me because I could have comforted her but sometimes the last person a daughter can trust is her mother.

Even though she belittles my psychicness, I think Susan and my sister have finally admitted to themselves that I do have the power to foresee the future and the past and I can call things exactly as they do happen.

PART II

Dreams of Prophecies

Profile Of The Madonna

I dreamed the following prophecy on August 10, 1994. I heard someone calling me. I searched for the location of the voice. Looking up, I found the voice belonged to our lady of sorrows. It was as if we were in a church without walls. As she is found in most churches, she was perched on a pedestal. The pedestal she was standing on looked like it was for a miniature statue. Her statue was in the size and form of a human. I wondered how this statue, almost a perfect human form could be set upon a ledge intended for a miniature statue.

I gazed at her. The color of her robe was a brilliant shade of blue. I noticed that she was wearing a white gown underneath the robe. The gown had the design of a heart elegantly embroidered in the center of her chest. Even from the great distance between us, I saw the perfection of the embroidered heart. There was not a better or more fitting place for it to be as she is one of total beauty. The heart began glowing as if a candle had been placed inside of it. I watched it in fascination.

As the heart began to glow, she began to take the steps of a human form. She was before me and just as clear as a real person is. The beautiful blueness of her robe flowed behind her and it seemed to me that the white of her gown had become more brilliant than it had previously been. The glow of the heart became larger and larger. Eventually, her whole being was enveloped in the glow. It was a beautiful golden glow that was shooting out in all directions.

Never, even in a dream, have I seen a sight more beautiful than this. This lady was truly pure in every way. I wondered why she was coming in human form to me. I was afraid that I had done something terribly wrong and she was here to reprimand or punish me for it. I thought it possible my most dreaded fear; simply going to hell may take place.

She began speaking to me. As she spoke, she came toward me with her aura glistening in all directions. It was as if sunbeams were shooting out. Her voice was crystal clear. I know I shall hear it again if when I die, I go to Heaven. The voice of the Madonna said to me, "You are the one chosen to help our people with prophecies. I have selected you and only you to give this secret information to." Stunned I said, "Why me? I'm not worthy of it. As hard as I try to understand, I still swear I'm the last person on the earth that should be giving this prophecy." To quiet me, she put her fingers to my mouth and said, "God has chosen you. I have chosen you. You are the only one I will give these numbers to. You will know the prophecy and you will tell the people in time." I said, "Wait a minute!" She replied, "No, I will not say these numbers to you twice. You must remember. They will not be given to you again until just before the prophecy is to be fulfilled."

I didn't once take my eyes off of her, afraid she might disappear or that I may not see the numbers at all. Suddenly, the numbers appeared to me. It looked like they were on a long, narrow white sheet of paper. Each number was very distinct. Each of the numbers had seven digits. They were all spiritual or psychic numbers. She showed the numbers to me again. I said, "Wait a moment. Let me get paper to write them down or I will forget." She said, "You will not forget them. Do not fear, you will remember them. You are the only one in this world that will have them. When the time is right, the numbers will come to you and you will know the reason the numbers are the key. Do not forget. Do not lose them. Wait for the time." "Wait a minute," I said, "I need to talk to you more. Don't leave me now!"

She started shrinking backwards, becoming smaller and smaller. Again, she became the small Madonna set on the shelf. The way she had first appeared to me in the dream. She was no longer life size. I had a terrible sadness in my heart with the thought that I may never see her again.

I awoke, completely stunned in the morning. Why had I been given such numbers and what did the numbers mean, I wondered. I spent the next three days speaking with the closest people I knew of any psychic value. I let them see the numbers. Hoping that by some stroke of luck we would be able to understand them. We translated them to different forms. We tried all of the different methods of ABC but it was to no avail. I had a friend who was a high ranked official in the Navy. He knew cryptography very well and knew how to decipher codes. He worked on my patio for an entire evening trying to understand the code. He began with numerology, changing the numbers backwards and forwards. He also could not make heads or tails of the numbers. The numbers created gibberish words that neither of us understood. I became depressed and afraid that I would not be able to remember the numbers. What if I was never called to give the numbers, I thought along with the fear that the world may be lost because of me.

Two or three weeks had passed before I gave the numbers to a friend. This valuable friend throughout the course of my years was also highly psychic. Both of us have premonitions and see prophecies or dreams. I told him that the numbers were a puzzle to me and asked him to please help me with it. He could always find an answer for just about anything. He said he would know what to do with them or whom they need to be taken to. After much deliberation on his part, he handed the numbers back to me. I said, "What do they mean?" And he replied, "I don't know what they mean." I was filled with bitter disappointment and thought no one would ever know what the numbers meant. I was very depressed and upset. I said to him, "I will not have lived up to what I am supposed to do." He said, "Don't be upset. Only you are supposed to know these numbers otherwise I would know them too. Don't be depressed Joyce, when the time is right these numbers will come back to you. The only thing I can say is that they are all spiritual numbers. You are a highly spiritual person and you have been given this message and these numbers from the Madonna and from God. They will tell you when the time is right."

In one way, I was sad because I just could simply not be with or see her again. But, I am looking forward to the time that she will reappear and tell me what the numbers mean. Every night I pray in my heart that I will be worthy of the dreams and the prophecies that are coming to me at such a rapid pace. I know that within time I must tell the world of all of my prophecy dreams. Preparing my people and the ones that are chosen to prophecy too. I must let the people know that the world is very near to coming to an end.

I pray for each and everyone on a nightly basis to find peace and happiness in their hearts before this day appears. Also, I wish to thank Jim who has been a devoted friend and who has tried with all of his heart to help me with the prophecies. He has tried to help me go on helping other people. I truly appreciate him and I hope he finds peace in this lifetime, before the end comes. I also would like to thank Bill. I wish for him to find the peace and love within his heart and may his heart be fulfilled for the little part he played trying to help me solve this puzzle by giving it all to God. This prophecy has yet to be revealed to me – when the time is near.

Prelude to The Bombs in North Korea

B efore we continue onto the next section of the book I would like to explain a few things. I've wondered a thousand times in my dreams why I'm the key character in this book. I have never been to New York and why the year of 1917? I wasn't even born then. Why North Korea? The government had never mentioned even the slightest hint that they might be there. All of my prophecies are in story form and have been since I was eleven years old. I would tell my mother and she'd say, "You are telling me fairy tales." She never believed they could possibly be anything else. As I grew older, I realized God had sent these prophecies to me in story form so as not to instill fear in people. The story unfolds as an everyday life occurrence, taking our days in stride, dealing with whatever comes along the way. We all have the same gift from God, the ability to listen to our inner voice and deal with the situation at hand accordingly. For some reason I seem to be on the next level and am just a little more "tuned" in.

There are countless clues in this section of the book and still I questioned whether or not my dreams were accurate. My sister read the entire sequence of The Hidden Bombs in

North Korea and said what a wonderful love story it is with a such a nice ending. But she also questioned why New York and why 1917? The plain and simple truth at that time was I just didn't know. I began to doubt whether or not the hidden bombs existed. Why would I dream of such a thing? Soon, the answers came to me in a way even I would never have imagined.

While working on the book I didn't leave the house except for business and household matters that couldn't be ignored. One evening my roommate asked if I would go with her to listen to some live music. It had been months since I'd had any dreams but I still sat around hoping each night would be the night God would answer my two remaining questions which were what is the mark of the beast and how will it affect us. I wanted to be able to tell everyone the best places to go in order to be safe. For my roommate's sake, I hesitantly got up and dressed to go to our usual place to listen to music. It was nearly ten o'clock when we arrived and the place was near empty. We took one of the tables nearest the door where we sat facing the band. Memories of a businessman from Washington began flooding my mind. He had business in town and this had been our place when he was here. We'd had so many good times together and I often wondered what had happened to him. A man got up from his bar stool and headed toward the door. He stopped and said hi to my roommate, Betty on his way out, obviously they knew each other. I began gathering my things to leave as well when I felt someone staring at me. When I turned around and saw it was John, the man I had dated, I was so shocked I was speechless. It had been four years since I had seen or heard from him and yet there he was. I couldn't believe my eyes at first and then I wondered what the odds of this happening were? One in a million for sure, but there he was, still staring at me. John re-entered my life at the same hour we originally met and we dated again for the exact same period of time as before. Oddly enough, it was this man who reassured me of the validity of my prophecies and the accuracy of the book.

I was busy with clients one day when John picked up my book and began reading. He had many questions for me, why did I write this, how did I have this information, where had it come from, and so on. I explained that these were my dreams, hence the title, "Dreams of Prophecies". He looked distressed and said, "You're giving away secrets." It was then and there I knew my book was meant to be. With a puzzled look on his face, he asked again and again where this information had come from. He was returning to Washington that night and was unable to finish the book. Although I know he had every intention to return, fate must have stopped it because that was the last I saw of him, he was transferred to another position when he returned. After a while, I stopped writing to him. I was certain I would never see him again, our time together was finished.

North Korea is popping up in the news. As you know, I originally wrote this book in 1995. I knew then that they had the bombs and that they've had them all this time. I hope you enjoy this next section and you recognize the clues which are included in it. It may seem like a love story but it is so much more.

The Bombs in North Korea

I dreamed of this prophecy in the year of 1917 on March the twenty-third.

Laverne and I lived in a small flat located on the edge of town in New York. It was the busier area of town before it dwindled away to poor residential areas, small businesses and basically was occupied with people of a lower class. I lived with a woman who was my companion as well as business associate; her name was Laverne. Laverne was a sweet and outgoing person with blue/green sparkling eyes, dishwater blonde hair, a beautiful face and an exquisite heart of pureness and lightness. Her every ounce of breath was filled with care, love and wishing others well. This lady was truly spiritual in every way and form. Laverne and I had known each other for many years; together we became associates and roommates via a reading I had done for her many, many years ago. She was very intuitive in the sayings and prophecies of the Bible. She dealt with people in an outgoing, friendly manner. She was uncanny about people and emotions and never missed anything going on in or around our element.

In New York, 1917 brought two distinct classes of people – the very elite and wealthy or the very poor. I always considered myself as being stranded somewhere between these classes. I made enough money from my office for Laverne and I to live comfortably. I did floral arrangements, funeral arrangements and wedding arrangements but most of all I counseled people. I tried to make these people understand that through change or faith they could begin new pathways of life. These paths would bring new direction transcending his/her life for the better. I also read Tarot cards and in some parts of the country this was deeply frowned upon. Through word of mouth, I became well known. Nine years of hard work in New York City brought me a relatively lucrative business consisting of reading Tarot cards and I was often called upon to mid-wife for the lower class families. Mid-wifing was not unusual at that time because unless it was a life and death matter, very few of the people who lived in the lower section of New York could afford doctor.

A lot of people thought it strange that I was now in my early thirties and had never been married. I had not even dated anyone. I remained a spinster through the course of my life. On the other hand, Laverne had been married but years ago became a widow. Laverne and I believed that through the course of fate and the hand of God we were brought together. The reasons and purposes for this had not been fully revealed to either of us but we were very comfortable with our way of life. We took each day as today and looked forward to tomorrow.

I arose early in the morning knowing that it would be just another day for me. On my desk, I had a lot of correspondence and work to take care of. Looking out of the windows, I noticed a grayish film on them from the soot of the city. They needed a good cleaning. The sun was beginning to filter through. The morning sun always felt good but as soon as it began shining in through the windows gray clouds would take it away. Instead of starting the things I should have begun, suddenly (for the first time in many years) I felt apprehension towards the day. For unknown reasons, I also felt fear.

I went to the window and looking out, I saw people beginning their new day. Scurrying along the walkway, the milkman was ringing his bells letting the people know that he was coming with the milk. I glanced into the sky and saw that large, dark, foreboding clouds had obscured the sun. The wind came up and it looked as if rain would come before the end of the day instead of sunlight. I turned away from the window, walked back to my desk and sat down. I began separating the mail. I had been at this chore for nearly an hour when I heard the phone ringing in our back apartment. Laverne picked up the phone. I knew that when she was through taking a message or conversing with the caller she would come to tell me who it had been; therefore, I tuned out the conversation, returning to my mail. Sorting the letters that I had at this time not been able to respond to, I figured this time would be as good as any to start. I reached into my desk and gathered my pen, paper and envelopes. I opened one letter at a time and began writing the answers to the questions the letter had asked me. I had barely two paragraphs on the page when Laverne came to the door. She said, "Mrs. Simms is on the phone. She's in labor and she walked to the nearest block to phone you. She wondered if you would be able to come and see her through with her labor and help with the children so she can lay down?" I told Laverne to tell Mrs. Simms that I was on my way. Vera was Mrs. Simms first name; I believe that I call her Mrs. Simms because her age is somewhere in the early fifties and it astounded me that the lady was still child bearing.

From the hallway coat rack, which stood by the door, I reached for my long, blue/gray coat. It was made of wool and went clear down to my ankles. The umbrella was underneath my coat but in my haste to get started, I forgot all about it. I raced down the steps, two at a time, buttoning my coat along the way. There was a chill factor to the wind; it was spring but it felt more like winter. Darker clouds were circling around the Heavens above our heads. I knew before the day was over it would rain, for sure.

I had walked around half of an hour before reaching the home of the Simms'. Three of the older girls were standing in the yard waiting for my arrival. The yard was in pathetic condition. Half of the picket fence was once painted white but now, it was a grayish color. The other half of the fence was missing and the path to the house had huge holes dug up by the dog. The girls spoke to me, Mrs. Simms knew I'd arrived and came to the door. Her hands were placed on her lower abdomen and it was obvious that she was in a lot of pain.

From her previous labors, Mrs. Simms' labors had a tendency to be quick and easy. I hoped this one would go well for her but this was not the case to be. The day wore on and she was having a very difficult time. Her husband came home, very tired from the ordeals of his day. Anxiously, he walked over to his wife and found her very flushed and in an extreme amount of pain. Mr. Simms walked over to me and asked if there was anything he could do to help. I told him to take the children to the nearby park so that they could get out of the house and play. I also told him I felt that the delivery would be soon. In consent, he nodded his head and one by one the children followed him out the door to play in a vacant field.

An hour later, Mrs. Simms delivered a son. After I washed and cleansed the baby, I showed him to the proud mother and asked what his name would be. She said that she hoped her husband would find David an agreeable name for their new son. I then cleaned up the mess the delivery had left, picked up the house and started dinner for Mrs. Simms and her family. I began to think about Mr. Simms. He looked as if he was all done in from manual labor at his age and also from the stress and strain of keeping his family together. The soup that I had prepared for Mrs. Simms had been on the stove boiling and cooking for quite some time. I had her sit up in bed and slowly fed her. When this was completed, I put the dish into the sink and went forward to my coat, which lay across a chair. I told Mrs. Simms that I would look in on her tomorrow but if she needed help before then to send one of her children for me.

I opened the door, walked into the yard and saw Mr. Simms and the children coming towards me. Even from a distance, I could see the stress on Mr. Simms face. His wispy, gray, thinning hair was blowing in the breeze. It was then that I realized that a misty rain was coming down and it was cold. I felt guilty because I had sent them out for a journey into weather that was not fit for a person to be in. The children lagged behind Mr. Simms (he was rushing towards the door) looking frightened of what I may have to say. When Mr. Simms reached me I was beaming with pride. I shook his hand and said, "Mr. Simms, you have a new son!" I laughed a little at him and said, "I hope this is the last child. Your wife had a very difficult labor and it's time that you call it quits." Mr. Simms nodded in full agreement promising that this was the end of the children; there would be no more. With that, I hugged him closely because I knew he was very worried about his wife's condition. I told him that she was okay but if she needed help to send for me and I would return immediately.

I had no more than spent ten minutes on the journey towards my apartment in the lower upper part of town when it began to rain in earnest. The rain was almost cold enough to turn to snow; it was a biting cold and also extremely windy. After fifteen minutes of walking, I noticed it was growing dark. I sped my pace, longing to be out of the rain. I had indeed had a long day; I was tired, cold and hungry. During the course of the day there had not been time to eat. I was going just as fast as my legs would carry me towards home. In the rush forward to my residence, my shoe slipped on a protruding rock loose in the cement walkway. I quickly brushed myself off with the full intention of resuming my hasty pace. I did not like this lower part of town. While helping myself up, I happened to glance back. I saw two men and they were following me. A chill ran up my spine. For as long as I can remember this was a premonition and meant that something was about to change the course of the day. Most assuredly, it was going to change the course of my life and suddenly I was afraid. I started to walk even faster; the rain was only a drizzle and this helped my pace. As I sped up, so did they and I knew without a doubt that they were following me. I had a horrible fear and chills still running up my spine. This was not a good omen; these men had some kind of malice towards me.

There was an alley way and I saw an opening in it. With my discovery, the last ray of light disappeared and total darkness surrounded me. I raced down the alley. The nearest buildings to me were on the left hand side. I stopped and held myself against the wall as closely as I could because the men had followed me into the alley way and at any moment I expected them to tear around the side of the building. I began praying that I would find a door at the rear of these buildings. That, by the hand of God and fate, I would be able to enter one of these doors, reaching safety from the two men that intended to harm me. I found a door, sped inside and slammed it shut. Fumbling for a lock, midway down the door I found a deadbolt. I bolted the lock just as fast as my frozen hands allowed me.

The room was in the back part of some building and it was cold. I simply stood still and after awhile became adjusted to the darkness. The smell of stale fruit and apples was apparent and I realized this must be the back of a storeroom for a restaurant or some kind of store. I eased myself to the floor and huddled there with my wet coat as close to my body as possible. I was shivering not only from the cold but also fear. Moments later, I heard gravel moving caused by someone's walking feet. I knew it was the two men searching for me. I was puzzled – why in the world were these two men after me? I had never seen either of them before but I assure you, I would know them anywhere if I were to see them again.

One of the men was wearing a dark, gray suit and a derby hat of the same color. He was in a way heavy set and around six inches shorter than the man walking beside him. This other man was dressed in all black attire and did not have a hat hiding his balding head of hair. He was a very tall man and could have easily passed as a boxer or wrestler. Indeed, a well built man; a bit heavy set but his body was firm. He must run or exercise on a daily basis, I thought. They were not poor men by any means but they were men on some sort of mission. Yes, I would know these two men I would know them anywhere.

I still heard the gravel munching under their feet. I knew that they continued to search for me in the darkness. At that moment, when they neared the door, I started shaking all over. The chill of the night and the wetness of my coat were nothing compared to the fear that was in my throat, threatening to strangle me. At this moment, I knew I must get a hold of myself. I had to believe and trust in God and whatever was going to happen was a destiny. And, with the shrewdness of my mind I would be able to get out of the predicament that I had put myself in. With these thoughts in mind, I became very calm and began thinking of a way to get myself out of this predicament. I must've sat there for an hour, hearing the footsteps in the alley fade away. I knew the men had were gone. I wondered if the rain outside had stopped. If it had, it would be easier to walk home in but then again the rain and drizzle would give me additional protection. I began to pray for God, for guidance and above all, asked my spiritual dark man (not of this world, a Protector) to come forth to lead and guide me safely home. I stayed in the building for a half of an hour or more until I knew I must take the chance and leave this building. Laverne would be extremely worried about me.

I opened the door and looked outside until my eyes adjusted to the darkness of the night. I saw no one and except for the room that I had found there was absolutely no place to hide in the alley way. The alley was a clean sweep from beginning to end. As I looked down the alley I saw my worst fear come forth; the alley came to a dead end. Had God not answered my prayers and opened this door I was still standing in, I would have been trapped. They would have caught me and surely had their way with me, doing whatever they had intended to do.

Carefully, I crept to the end of the building and peered down both sides of the street. There were no buildings on the other side of the street. However, there was one danger, a long forgotten park. Weeds and brush were overgrown.

I remembered that there was once a pond but weeds concealed it from view. Not even a trace of the pond's existence remained. Even the image was gone. Tall trees with budding leaves hung overhead. The rain was still drizzling down from the sky. Cautiously, I turned to the left and began walking down the street. Five minutes later, I noticed that even my hand was not visible. Complete darkness surrounded me. However, the men appeared to be nowhere and I sighed in relief. It was as if they had simply vanished into the night.

An uncanny feeling came over me; they might know where I live and could easily be watching my apartment building. I knew that I would have to be extremely careful because I did not want to put myself in a situation like this again. I decided not tell Laverne what had happened tonight because I knew how frightened she would be for me. There was no need for that so I began to calm myself. I decided to not tell anyone about what had happened. Laverne would believe any explanation I gave to her concerning the time of my arrival. I would simply make it clear that Mrs. Simms labor had been long and difficult. Laverne knew the Simms didn't have a phone and would not have a second thought about my explanation. I did not like to keep this from her or for that matter keep anything from her. In this situation, I decided protecting her from fear and worry was more important.

The rain had become more brisk and was peppering down upon my head and coat. I was chilled to the bone; my coat was soaked and the sidewalk was full of puddles that completely soaked my shoes and feet. I wished I'd taken the umbrella with me this morning. At long last, I came to the steps of the apartment building that contained my office and in the rear, my home. Because my hands were shaking so intensely, I was not able to find the keys inside of my purse. As the last resort, I pounded on the door and waited for Laverne to open it.

I saw through the front window with the curtains closed that the gas light in the office was still burning. Laverne first appeared in the sitting area. She walked through the office, opened the front door and saw that I was soaked clear through. Saying not one word, she calmly came towards me to assist taking my coat off.

Standing in the entryway, she said, "I'll get you a hot cup of coffee to help warm you up. I also have the gas fire in the fireplace going. It's been a bad day. What kept you so long?" I began reciting the speech I'd prepared for her, "Mrs. Simms had a hard and difficult labor. When it was over, I prepared dinner for the family and made sure everyone was settled in." Laverne gave me a very funny look; the shrewdness of her looks make you feel as if she can see into your soul. I thought to myself, this lady did not believe my story for even a moment. For a split second, I was worried but then a sweet smile appeared on her face.

Laverne was a woman that expected people to eat and enjoy her food because she enjoyed fixing it for them. Soon, she was hurrying out from the kitchen with a steaming bowl of soup, a sandwich and a large cloth napkin. Laverne put the napkin on my lap and then sat down in her chair to watch me eat. I was starving because this was the first thing I ate all day. I finished the half of my sandwich and the last spoonful of soup; I could eat no more. The moments of the day began flooding my mind, my throat was closing up which made getting the last bite of food down hard. As I relived this evening's experience, fear welled in my throat.

Casually I told Laverne I needed to take a good hot bath, to put my robe on and snuggle in my bed. Looking at the timepiece on the mantle, I realized it was almost ten o'clock in the evening. Usually, both Laverne and I were in bed by this time. Indeed, it had turned out to be a very long day.

That night, before tucking myself in bed, I knelt down to the floor. I thanked God, my spiritual man and fate for guiding my footsteps safely home. With that, I climbed into bed. I was asleep before my head had reached the pillow. For the first few hours, I slept fitfully, tossing and turning. I jumped at the mere sound of rain hitting the window. I became afraid of every strange sound I heard. I realized it would take a few days to regain any sense of security. A few minutes later, I could hear something or someone prowling near my window. Startled, I jumped out of bed and ran to the window. I saw nothing. The tree that branched out over our small yard caused the noise. The wind was blowing, causing one of the tree's limbs to touch my window.

I saw that it was still raining and glanced at the timepiece sitting beside my bed. It was 4:15 in the morning. Seeing the time, I retraced my footsteps, got into bed and tucked myself in. I fell sound asleep and began to dream.

I was dreaming of the two men that had followed me the day before. The setting was different. Sprawling, old, oak trees surrounded a white building. There were white pillars holding verandahs that circled the house. It resembled a plantation. I was in awe; I had never seen a house with such beauty. Could there possibly be a place, anywhere in the world, with the beauty of what I was seeing? The men lurked behind a huge tree. It was as if they were in hiding, just watching and waiting. I knew they weren't waiting for me because I would never be in a house of such luxury. I dreamed on. I saw myself working at the desk in my office, dealing and shuffling papers around. I was looking out of the window, across the street at the abandoned park, listening to the birds sing from the trees. Outside, the day was bright and sunny. Still dreaming, I heard Laverne call from the doorway.

Laverne and I always had dinner early in the evening and ate a small snack before we went to bed. I looked into the sky and saw that it was late in the afternoon. The sun would be setting soon. I was glad to see the sun and people strolling along the street enjoying it's warm rays. The chill of the previous night had prevented this sight. I knew I was taking a risk by leaving the large, front windows uncovered. This was all right with me because I needed the light and I needed to experience the warmth the sun was giving to me. These days, it seemed to be the only thing that rejuvenated my spiritualness and self esteem.

I went to bed early and the dream began where it had left off the previous night. During the course of the dream, I tossed and turned until I fell off of the bed. I awoke, climbed back up to my bed and sat on the edge wondering what had made me so distressed. It was as if I had had a nightmare. After a short time, I recalled the dream. Again, I was at the white home, which was surrounded by acres of sprawling lawn and big, oak trees. There was a large group of people, including the two men. They were slipping from tree to tree and watching me. I was wearing a long, white dress. What did all of this mean? I seldom wear white because creme is a better color for me and I don't own a dress resembling the one in the dream.

From all of my past experiences, I knew that this was some kind of symbol. I never have idle dreams. There is always reasons and purposes or prophecies to be entailed in my dreams. I couldn't understand or comprehend this dream. Why the white house, the same men and what does it mean? Once again, I eased myself into bed, tucking in my blanket clear up to my chin. Suddenly I was cold and I felt chilled. I wondered if this dream only entailed me. I decided to fight the urge to sleep; I would stay awake until morning came. Within half of an hour, I was dreaming. The postman delivered a long, white envelope to my door. Strangers living in a foreign place had sent the envelope to me. Inside was an invitation to visit and stay with these people. My dream diminished after that and I saw that the darkness was slipping to dawn. Peacefully, I slept for another two hours before beginning the new day.

Between the dreams, what had happened with the men and the fact that I couldn't confide these things to Laverne, I had a difficult time settling myself down so that I could begin the day's tasks. I had several appointments scheduled for this afternoon and I did not wish to keep any of them. How could I bring myself to such a spiritual state? One that would allow these people to be enlightened by my assurance of safety and destiny would be wonderful to them. Indeed, lately all I was able to think of was the disturbance caused by the two men. It had changed me, spiritually. The incident reared it's head into an element that I was afraid to dive into. I feared it coming forth and fully presenting itself in my life. What I think and feel, my thought forms often become my reality. By silencing the voice in my head, I hoped to overcome this, warding it off. If it was a destiny than I was going to walk around it. If at all possible, prevent its occurrence.

The fifth day after the incident, I could no longer avoid leaving my home. I had to visit with the sick and deliver flower bouquets to the chapel and the undertaker. I had to go out today, there was no way around it. When I awoke, I set a firm course of action for the day. I rapidly ate a breakfast of toast and tea. I got my coat from the rack and put it on while looking at myself in the mirror hung on the sidewall. I gathered the papers and other miscellaneous items I needed along with the flower bouquets to deliver. I walked briskly down the steps and into the street.

The chill from the rain was gone and it was a beautiful, warm morning. The park's grass, trees and bushes were bright green. The bulbs, daffodils and early tulips were bursting forth, creating an exquisite array of colors. The yellow of the daffodils was the predominant color. The rain had caused one good thing – spring had burst forth. It sprouted its' colorful creatures into being and they were embracing the sunlight with their heads. It was picturesque. Suddenly, I was glad to be alive. It was a new and wonderful day. With that thought in mind, I began to sing. Not giving another thought to the men or the dreams.

My elected chores took far longer than I had expected. It was around four in the afternoon when I finished visiting with the last person I intended to see. Anna saw me to the door and I casually began my walk home. I took my time. All I wanted was to feel and enjoy the peacefulness of the day.

Upon returning home, I found Laverne and dinner waiting for my arrival. We closed the office, putting the closed sign in the window, strolled to the rear and entered our small home. During dinner, we conversed about the day's events. What each of us had done and the gossip heard while I traveled around town were the main topics. The evening's warmth wore on. There was no need to light the gas log in the fireplace so we simply sat in the office, basking in the warmth of the sun's last rays. We relaxed in the safety we felt within our home and within ourselves.

For several days, I slept peacefully. It seemed that my dreams and nightmares had disappeared. After a while, the men and the white house on it's large estate dimmed from my memory – almost forgotten. Believing these dreams were caused by fear consoled me. It was not possible that they were a prophecy about me or of what was yet to come.

When I arose the next morning, I decided to visit the sick and the home of the Simms. Dread was felt when I thought of revisiting the Simms but it was something I needed to do. I decided never to go to their home in the evening and in the morning light I slowly began retracing my steps. The way to the Simms' home brought all of the memories of the men back to me. As if a premonition, I felt a chill rise up my spine. I wondered if the men or someone I hardly knew were connected to what I had just felt. If this were not a prophecy to me but to them, would it ever be revealed to me?

Upon reaching the Simms' home, I learned that Jake, Mrs. Simms husband and she had named the baby David. Now, I might be a spinster at thirty but I certainly adore children. I bounced David up and down in my lap. I rocked him in my arms while singing a lullaby, enjoying this time. Mrs. Simms was in adequate condition considering the ordeal of her labor. This was her fifth child and she was beaming in pure delight over him. During the day, the other children attended school and her husband worked. She had a chance to rest while they were gone. She needed it. When her family came home, her grueling work began. This work took hours and often lasted late into the night.

Mrs. Simms and I visited for around two hours. In the course of this time, I was offered tea and a slice of her homemade bread. The bread was so delicious and I asked for the recipe. Mrs. Simms was enchanted by my request and was more than willing to fulfill it. The fact that I was so comfortable with her made her beam with pride. I did not live in the lower part of town and being here now, I was in no way bothered. My train of thought had never compared her side of town to mine – the differences were not worthy enough to take time comparing.

Mrs. Simms was a human being. A beautiful one both spiritually and in her soul. This lady had a pure heart of gold. She'd lived a hard life and was married at the age of sixteen. She truly loved her family and home. Mrs. Simms was happy. I thought to myself about the lesson from all of this and how great the value of it is. It makes no difference where we are or what dwelling we reside in because true happiness is found and belongs within our hearts. If our soul is pure we shall not worry about the roof over our heads. Nor shall we worry about with whom or where our associations happen to be. **We are all one in the same.**

My days seemed to conglomerate into each other. Almost a month had passed since the incident with the men. I had almost put it behind me. And then, on a bright and sunny afternoon, the postman came to my door. Laverne was out with friends and I was working in my office. Enjoying the fact that spring had sprung in New York, I decided this was the time to straighten my desk and take care of any unfinished business. I went to the door and greeted the postman. He handed me some bills and then a long, white envelope. With surprise, I looked at the postman because I couldn't identify any postage mark on the envelope. A chill ran up my spine. I thanked the postman and returned to the office.

Chills come to me only at very certain times. I receive them if I'm reading somebody, telling a prophecy that will absolutely come true or when I'm going to go through a prophecy.

Seeing the letter that lay, half unfinished, I put the mail aside. I finished the letter and decided to call it a day. I had been working for a few hours and felt caught up with most of my work. Spring was getting to me and I wanted to enjoy it. I took the mail and a book with me into our small backyard. The yard was surrounded by a tall, brick wall with a gate that lead to the open fields behind the building. The small yard consisted of a little patch of green grass, some forgotten flowers, a few bushes and a large, old tree. When the wind blew, the tree's branches would brush against the building and my bedroom window. Trees are a big part of nature and I liked this one especially because it shaded the yard and circling it, was a bench that was built many years ago. At one time, this had probably been a beautiful yard. I sat down on the bench and made myself comfortable. In the limbs above my head, birds were singing and I began to hum along as I opened the white envelope.

The beginning of the letter made no sense to me. It was an open invitation to visit the home of the letter's senders. As I read on, it explained a bit more. While visiting New York, a friend of theirs' had come to see me as a prophesier and psychic reader. This friend was very impressed and told these people of my work. They were very interested in meeting me. In the hopes of my acceptance, their offer included my companion, Laverne.

The offer's accommodations included round trip train tickets to Virginia. Upon our arrival, there would be a spacious house to stay in, large enough that Laverne and I would each have our own rooms. During our stay, I would be doing readings for people living as far as North Carolina. The letter went on stating that this would advance my career and I could even become widely well known. I stopped reading the letter. For a minute I was in awe. Was this actually happening? This could open up a whole new world to me; open a whole new door. The chances of something like this happening to me had to be one in a million, I estimated. Why was this offered to me? Why was this made available to me during this part of my life? Before I had completed the letter, chills began to run up my spine. They swept throughout all of my body; chilling my entire essence.

My first instinct was to say no. There had to be something wrong with the invitation. I have been a reader since the age of sixteen. No one has ever made an offer to me like this before. Why did I receive such a thing in this part of my life? I told myself to set the letter aside. There was no point in continuing to read it. When I went inside, I would simply throw the letter into the garbage and entirely forget it. So, after folding the letter back into the envelope, I set it beside me. I began to read my book.

After reading a whole chapter, I found concentrating to be impossible. I couldn't recall any of what I had just read. Evidently, the letter's invitation was disturbing me more than I'd realized. I began debating with myself, should I or should I not finish reading the letter? I consoled myself – go-ahead reading the letter doesn't obligate you to accepting the offer. Slowly, I took the letter out and found the paragraph that earlier, I had quit reading. I began reading the rest of the letter. It said if I accepted the invitation then at the end of a two-day weekend I would receive a sum of two thousand dollars, in cash. During the weekend, I would entertain the other guests by doing readings for them. When I was finished with this they welcomed me to stay as a guest and enjoy their hospitality. The letter said it would give me a chance to see the sights of Virginia. Considering that I've never really traveled anywhere; I thought to myself what a wonderful chance this would be to increase my knowledge of history. A calling card with their name and address was enclosed. A second postage paid envelope was also enclosed.

Whether I accepted or not, I was asked to send a reply. The letter was signed by Richard Robinson. The name sounded respectable. His name was different than the one on the calling card. I picked the calling card and read the name, Martha Simpson. I decided the letter did not need to be brought to Laverne's attention. However, as the time approached dinner, I decided that Laverne did need to know of the offer. In order for me to accept the offer, I knew she would have to come along as my companion and my associate. It would be necessary to have her help. Needing her to accept this offer meant I needed her to turn it down. The dinner table overlooked the yard that most of my afternoon had been spent in. An hour had passed since my decision and the sunlight was fading away. To bring the last of the light in, the door and curtains were wide open.

We were almost through with dinner when I reached into my pocket for the letter. I simply handed it to Laverne. A surprised look appeared on her face. I knew what this look meant. Her look asked, "What is the meaning of this?" My response, "Laverne, read it." I watched her as she read. Her eyes grew dark and misty. The shrewd and calculating look on her face meant a plan was brewing in her head. I knew that in her own due time she would inform me on what that plan was. Without saying a word, she folded the letter and set it beside me. She cleared the table and put the dishes into the sink. She was in silent council and discussing anything with her would be useless.

There was a small fire in the fireplace. Laverne and I were seated in our favorite chairs when our conversation about the letter began. I was surprised by Laverne's opinion. She felt the trip might bring us danger. After a long discussion, we agreed to sleep on the subject. In the morning, we would make a final decision and send the response to the Simpsons.

I heard Laverne late into the night. It sounded as if anxiety and restlessness had overcome both of us. My share was done by tossing and turning myself all over the bed. The happenings and decisions throughout the day had caused a lot of stress for me. I was fatigued and in spite of myself, I fell asleep. My dreams began, again. The large, white house and grounds was the setting of this dream. The house with its pillars and two-story balcony was not just a house it was a mansion. The grounds were covered with a multitude of enormous old trees and shrubs. All of the spring shrubs were blooming. Virginia had shrubs that were unknown to me. I was strolling around, taking in the exquisite beauty of the land when a chill ran up my spine. Someone was watching me; there was no doubt in my mind. With a fast stride, I set forth to the house. Out of the side of my eye, I caught a glimpse of a man wearing a black suit. In my dream, I instantly knew he was one of the men from New York. What was his connection to me? I had just seen him less than one month ago in New York. How could he be here, in Virginia now? After these thoughts to myself, the dream diminished.

I awoke groggy and unsettled. It was morning and for the first time in many months, I was up before Laverne. This was a sign that her night had been very bad. She awoke looking very tired. Dark circles were under her eyes. I was almost too afraid to approach her. I knew she had very little sleep and she was still disturbed. I wouldn't speak of the letter until we had finished a hearty breakfast. I felt that we would need a lot of energy in order to decide on anything.

That afternoon, neither of us was very hungry. The letter had not been discussed during breakfast. It was as we settled down to a light lunch and tea that the subject of the letter began. Thoughts from the night before began to unfold. Again, Laverne expressed her feeling that the trip may lead us into danger. I, on the other hand, didn't remember my dream from the night before; this in itself was unusual. After all of the tossing and turning I had done, I thought I'd slept soundly. In the morning, I felt I was ready to face the day and this decision. I verbalized to Laverne, "For the first time in my thirty years of life, I want adventure. I want to see the sights of the world. I want to be a challenge to these people I'll be reading for. I want to make contact with these people. This may start a new way of life for both of us. I want to go." After a while, Laverne nodded her head in agreement. "Obviously", she said to me "it must be a destiny that both of us go. And, go we shall! I'll bring you paper and a pen so that you can tell them that we will go."

It was the twenty-seventh of May when a second envelope from the Simpsons arrived. Inside, there was a brief message to thank us for accepting the offer. They said that the guests were excited and we would make many new friends during our stay. We would be welcomed with open arms. The envelope also contained two train tickets. We were to board the train on the sixth of June, ten days from now.

We would be gone for an indefinite period of time. By train, it would take nearly a week to reach Virginia. If we decided to stay when the weekend was over, we would be in Virginia for a full week. Another week would pass while we traveled home. If we were going to be gone for such a lengthy amount of time I had a lot of preparations to make. The house needed to be secure. Everything needed to be in order. The bills had to be paid, the refrigerators needed to be cleaned as well as the clothes we were going to take. Unsure of exactly what we needed to take, we also had to buy a few things; just in case. We packed for warm weather as we were told to do.

On the eve of our departure, we spoke of everything except the trip. We chatted about the bad times we had spent together, times spent in New York and the anticipation henceforth into the years of being together in the same element. If any desire to change our existence in New York was felt, it was not mentioned by either of us. Maybe subconsciously, each of us hoped the trip was a journey to a new destiny. Remembering all of the time we both had left to live on earth and wondering what was going to come. Neither of us said a word about it in our casual conversation. Murmuring goodnight to each other, we both retired to bed early. We needed to rise at six o'clock in the morning; it would be upon us soon.

We traveled to the train depot in an open carriage. In 1917, motor vehicles were available even to the lower class. However, Laverne and I chose to travel in buggies and carriages. This particular carriage was like a taxi. The driver carried our baggage to the sidewalk in front of the depot. After paying him with coins, Laverne and I retrieved our things and began our adventure by boarding the train.

The ride was not one of great comfort. Black smoke bellowed from the train. If the windows were open, cinders descended into the coach and settled onto your clothing. This caused a dismal mess. We slept upright in our chairs. The only exercise available was the walk to the dining car and to the rest rooms. The rest of the time was spent in our seats. We had brought books to read to help time pass. After five days, we arrived at the depot in Virginia.

Virginia was a beautiful state. Even from a great distance the magnificence of the scenery could be seen. We watched through the windows, able to take in the state's beauty before we had exited the train. The depot in Virginia was quite large. It was a lengthy building that expanded itself very close to the tracks. The conductor helped us with our baggage as we left the train.

We looked around and saw a chauffeur coming towards us. Dressed in a gray uniform with a cap, the man was dressed fashionably for 1917. To our surprise, a motorcar was waiting for us. I had never ridden in a car. Indeed, these people were extremely wealthy. Another man was sitting in the front of the car. He and the chauffeur chatted in low tones. The vehicle was traveling toward the countryside. Soon, paved roads were left behind and dirt roads took their place. The ride went on and on. An extensive amount of time passed before we reached our destination.

We were helped from the car and finally, I was able to view the Simpsons' home. A white two-story mansion surrounded by pillars and verandahs stood in front of me. There was a driveway that encircled the front yard of the mansion. A fountain stood in the middle, spurting water in all directions. The splendorous grounds matched what I had seen in my dreams.

As the front door of the house opened, Laverne and I received a warm greeting from the butler. He led us into the drawing room, which was simply magnificent. The ceiling was high and the floor was made of marble. French windows and doors accented the room. The doors opened onto a terrace that had a profusion of blooming flowers. As we entered, a stout and older looking woman made her way toward us. She introduced herself as Martha. She apologized for her husband's absence and promised we would meet him at dinner.

Martha assured us that our stay would be comfortable. She called for a maid and suggested we take a nap before dinner. Our journey had been long and indeed we were tired. Her suggestion sounded good and we agreed. A maid had arrived to show us to our rooms. After thanking our hostess, we followed the maid up a circling stairway that led to the left wing of the house.

A long corridor appeared at the top of the stairs. There were many doors, some opened and some closed. I followed the maid to the last door of the left wing. She said, "This will be your room," as she opened the door. She set my luggage down and then opened the French doors. As I walked out onto the balcony, I heard her saying that if I needed anything to pull the cord and she would return. Another maid had showed Laverne to the last door on the opposite end of the corridor. Inside of her room, she received the same experience I had.

I felt that it was somewhat odd for my companion and I to not be placed in adjoining rooms. Laverne and I were not used to being so far apart since we had lived close to each other for many years. But as I stood on the balcony, I noticed its length. The balcony connected the French doors of Laverne's room with mine. If I needed her, I would simply walk to her room on the balcony. A wrought iron railing protected me from falling onto the balcony below and I felt safe. Upon entering my room, I found a fresh bath had been drawn for me and towels had been placed in the bathroom. My nightgown was lying on the bed and the maid had placed my clothing into the chiffarobe along the wall that was opposite of the bed.

Our rooms were beautifully decorated with French furnishings of the eighteenth century. I wondered if the family that lived here in Virginia was of French descent; it seemed likely. After I had taken my bath and finished my toiletries, I enjoyed the softness of my nightgown. I snuggled myself beneath the sheets of the bed. As my head hit the pillow I was fast asleep.

The shadows of the evening had fallen on the verandah when I awoke. From my bed, I could see the sunset. I quickly rose out of bed, put on my robe and went to Laverne's room. I opened her door and became very surprised because she was not inside. It wasn't like Laverne to leave without letting me know of her whereabouts. Disturbed by her absence, I hurried to my room and dressed myself for the evening.

As I made my way down the winding staircase, I heard voices. They were coming from the balcony that lead to a stoned terrace. I knew this was where everyone must be. As soon as I had walked outside, Martha came over and introduced her husband, John to me. His thin frame stood around six feet, two inches. Martha looked tiny standing beside him. The intent of the stare that was coming from his blue eyes made me realize a few things. He could be firm about his wishes and possibly, he was not at all the man that his surface made him appear to be. This man, John needed to be watched closely.

In the height of her glory, Martha was bubbling around all of her guests. During the course of the evening, many people had been introduced to me. Drinks, ranging from lemonade, tea and the liquor of your choice were served on ice. This in itself was a luxury for me. As I glanced around the crowd, I did not see Laverne anywhere. She had disappeared, again.

Deeply disturbed, I walked over to my hostess to ask where I could find my friend. Martha patted my hand as she replied, "Laverne offered to help the others in the kitchen. The staff is short handed tonight and I eagerly accepted her offer." The smile on my face turned into a stern and solemn look. I was quite annoyed that my companion had been turned into a servant. Martha noticed my unhappiness with the situation. "If you're upset by this, I'll have a maid fetch Laverne immediately. Please accept my apology. I know Laverne is much more than a servant and she'll be back here, with us shortly," she said. I thanked her for understanding my feelings and moments later, Laverne appeared. She was swishing her way through the door in a light blue gown with ruffles around the high neck and long sleeves. I sighed in relief. My friend looked beautiful and seemed to be in a good state of mind.

Laverne looked like she was enjoying herself. I was overwhelmed by the strangers surrounding me. Laverne was experiencing much more pleasure than I was. The ease that I'd felt upon entering this house was gone. My nerves were raw and I was on edge. I'd become very sensitive towards sound and touch. I began walking to the outer edge of the terrace slipping away from the crowd.

I needed to observe these people – my host, hostess and their guests. This seemed to be the best chance I would have. Emerging myself into a forest of trees and dense foliage, I could breath a bit easier. There was a stone bench that faced the terrace to sit on. It was dark and the lanterns were softly glowing. I observed some innocent people and also some who seemed as if they were acting on a stage. A chill ran up my spine, indicating a premonition. Alone at the edge of the forest, I became uneasy. I swiftly made my way back into the crowd.

As soon as I had re-entered the main area of the terrace, dinner was called. French doors connected the terrace to the enchanting dining room. Another set of doors adjoined the long dining room to the grand ballroom. When the doors were opened all of the way, one enormous room was formed. This evening, the doors were ajar so the soft music that was being played on the piano, which sat in the far corner, could be heard during dinner. Flower arrangements were placed on each of the superbly set tables. Each seat was assigned to a guest; labeled by a name card.

As I was seated, I glanced to my left and saw a man seated next to me. In my head, I observed all of the guests I had seen or met earlier; he was not one of them. Surprised by this, I wondered what time he had arrived. Maybe he had been here before my arrival. Why had he not attended the social hour before dinner? I knew this man was a piece in my puzzle. Realizing this, a chill ran up my spine and shivers began traveling through my entire body. I was nervous and this man, sitting beside me was the cause. It was difficult to be friendly, outgoing, even to smile. I wanted to leave. Nothing sounded better than the thought of going upstairs and into my room.

Laverne and I sat on opposite ends of the table. Several chairs and conversations separated us. Each guest appeared to chat with whomever he or she was seated beside. The murmurs of these conversations made it impossible for me to communicate with Laverne. It didn't look as if this bothered Laverne; she seemed to be enjoying herself and the man sitting beside her. He looked to be in his late forties. He was a tall and thin man with a head of flaming red hair.

I didn't picture Laverne being attracted to someone of this description and the sight before my eyes was somewhat amusing. It was plain to see that she was having a wonderful time with him. A woman sat on her other side. Later on, I found out that her name was Jane. She was around nine years younger than her brother; the man with the red hair.

Her name was Jane and his was William. William preferred to have people call him Bill. I thought Bill was a simple name that fit this man's seemingly simple appearance. I remembered that looks could definitely be deceiving.

On several occasions, I felt the eyes of the man sitting to my left, staring at me. Sitting on my right hand side was a woman named Bea. We kept up a steady conversation throughout dinner. Ignoring Paul, the man to my left, eased my nerves a bit, especially when I could feel the eyes of the stranger that sat on my other side.

Bea's age was somewhere in the middle of her forties. Covering her petite frame was a light green gown. Her gown was both beautiful and fashionable. Her gorgeous blonde hair had been piled onto the top of her head. She was a delicate and exquisite woman with only a few lines around her mouth to distinguish her age.

The gentleman sitting to her right was her husband. He seemed friendly. When he spoke, I could hear a broken accent but I wasn't able to distinguish its' nationality. I wanted to know their nationality, where they lived and how far they had traveled to be guests here. I wondered if I would be able to ask them these questions, before the end of my stay.

This couple seemed to know Martha and John rather well. Actually, as I looked around the room, it seemed that everyone knew each other well. Paul was the name of the man sitting beside me. This was an average, common name but I knew that he was not an average or common person. His dark brown eyes appeared to be made of smoldering brown coals. He was another person that I would be closely watching. If any dealings took place between us, my part would be one of caution.

Finally, dinner came to an end. The party followed the host and hostess into the ballroom. Music began to play and people began to dance. French doors had been opened which created an open element between the ballroom and the balcony leading to the terrace.

The night air was filled with the sound of crickets and in the distance, a frog or two could also be heard. Because frogs always live in or around water, it seemed to be reasonable that a body of water was near the house. Those living in big cities – such as New York, seldom hear crickets. In order to hear the tune of these crickets, I walked onto the balcony and toward the terrace. I took no more than ten steps when I felt a hand gently rest upon my shoulder. I quickly turned around to see whom this hand belonged to. I saw the man, Paul who had sat next to me during dinner.

We began talking and Paul displayed the qualities of a perfect gentleman. He was a gracious host. He tried to make me comfortable in my surroundings. Before I could catch my breath, Paul began to ask a lot of questions. Some of these were quite personal questions and I sidetracked their answers. I didn't feel that he needed to know everything about me and I knew I wasn't going to know everything about him. After having a brief discussion, I suggested we go inside. I would feel safer inside. For a second, his mood changed. It seemed the color of his eyes had darkened. He expressed a look of disappointment and I didn't know why. And with that, we both went inside.

A few people asked me to dance. I accepted two of the requests; one made by the host and the other was made by Paul. When I finished my last dance, I made my way over to Martha and John. Begging their pardon, I excused myself after explaining that I had preparations to make in my room before tomorrow. I said goodnight and retired to my room. Before tucking myself into bed, I decided to view the grounds one more time. It wasn't long after I'd begun gazing from the balcony, when I heard Laverne's footsteps in the hallway. She entered her room and locked the door behind her. She walked across the room, opened her French doors and walked down to where I stood. We were both glad to be together and alone from everyone else. Before saying goodnight, we discussed the events of the day, the evening and those tomorrow would bring.

Morning arrived early and I had a lot of things to do before the afternoon. The functions that were taking place downstairs awoke me. As I looked down from the balcony, I saw servants preparing large tables. Momentarily, the purpose of my stay had been forgotten. I went inside instantly, realizing I had to set up my own tables for the readings I was to do this afternoon. Laverne and I would be very busy this morning and we had barely enough time to dress for it.

The activities of the day, including a luncheon would be outside. More guests had begun arriving and I knew that I didn't have much time to set up. I walked around outside circumnavigating the area of the home, searching for the spot where I wanted my table placed. The lawn sprawled in all directions. The entire estate was emasculate. Even the smallest shrubs and trees were manicured to perfection. I spent twenty minutes evaluating the grounds before I found a majestic, old oak tree. Its location was at the edge of the woods where grass gave way to the forest. The tree's branches sprawled out and would provide the shade for my table. As I had made this decision, Laverne was coming to assist me. Earlier, we had prepared packets of information to hand out as the guests were being read. She had unpacked the packets and the bundle was tucked beneath her arm.

Shortly after we'd prepared our table, laborers came to put up a tent. They placed curtains on all sides of the table, completely enclosing it. Although I preferred my back facing the tree, which allowed me to view in all directions, I said nothing as they left. I detested being enclosed as I sat at the table and decided to take matters into my own hands. It took me over an hour to take down the side curtains of the tent; I left the rear curtain hanging. Now, I had a view to my front and both of my sides and this greatly enhanced my comfort.

The verandah, in the front of the house (connected to the second floor's balcony) was being composed for an orchestra. A piano had been wheeled outside. The musicians had taken their places and they were now setting up their instruments. Opposite from where my table was set up, the yard was being prepared for the luncheon. A canopy stood over the buffet line, where the food was being arranged. It sat on the edge of the garden. Tables, each with a canopy overhead, had been prepared for the guests to sit, eat and visit at.

It seemed that everything was in its place for the afternoon. My table was ready; I was not. I retreated back to my room to bathe and dress for the occasion. Laverne followed, a few paces behind mine. As my assistant, she also needed to prepare herself for the afternoon. Today's work would earn us the two thousand dollars that the letter spoke of. Unbeknownst, was that we were about to earn much more than two thousand dollars; our earnings not in the form of cash but in the coming of knowledge.

After my bath, I looked through my wardrobe to select an outfit. I decided to wear an ivory colored dress with a powder blue sash. The dress was low cut with an opening in the front and whisping arms. Suddenly, out of nowhere, a maid appeared and was finishing the buttons on the back of my dress. In addition, she tightly wrapped the sash around my waist and sat me down in front of the dresser. She was very friendly and referred to me as "Missy". Her name was Susan.

As Susan brushed my long, red hair, she spoke non-stop. I don't think I would've been able to get a word in edgewise, even if I'd wanted to. I believe she was a bit excited about the afternoon with the youthfulness of her years. Before the end of my stay, Susan and I would become close friends. Susan twisted my hair up and loosely pinned it at the top of my head. When she had finished, I stood up, braced my shoulders and walked down the stairs of the balcony, through the terrace and out to the lawn.

Some of the guests were already outside, visiting among each other. In full motion, the orchestra had begun to play. The music selected for the occasion seemed very appropriate. All of the melodies were beautiful, some even haunting. By haunting, I mean that I had heard these pieces before, possibly in another lifetime.

Laverne joined me just as I was seating myself. All of the materials that we would need this afternoon were in place, at the table by the oak tree. I still needed to prepare my spiritual self for the proceedings that would begin directly after lunch. I looked around, observing the afternoon. It promised to be a warm one; there was not a cloud in sight.

I was grateful that our host and hostess were such thoughtful people and provided tents to shade their guests from the sun's heat. I had not seen much of Martha or John this morning. As I looked in the direction of their home, I saw Paul staring down at me from the second floor's balcony. I blushed in surprise. I wondered how long he had been looking down at me. I also wondered what his reasoning or purpose was. I glanced down at my papers. They were in perfect order but I was nervous. I looked back up at the balcony. Paul was gone.

People were beginning to gather near the buffet line. In fact, some had begun to eat their lunch early. I did not feel like milling around the crowd waiting to get my food. Actually, thinking about all of the readings I was about to do, I really wasn't very hungry. I asked Laverne if she would mind getting little portions of the lighter dishes for me. "Oh, gladly," she replied, "we can eat and relax together before we start to work." This was good because while she was gone I could meditate. I needed to become in tune with my inner soul. However, Laverne at my side always made me feel a bit more at ease. I was happy that we had this chance to be together before the afternoon's work began.

For more than an hour, people ate, drank and visited with each other. I was a little anxious for lunch to come to an end. When it finally did, the music began to play and Laverne began to work. She had a woven basket in her hand and people were all around her. Those interested in having a reading done were to give Laverne their name card. As she received them, she gave the guest a number. The readings would go in numerical order. I stood against the oak tree, waiting for Laverne to return with the basket. The basket would tell me how many readings I could expect to do.

I glanced across the spacious lawn. People, young and old, were milling around the tables that had been shaded by the tents from the noonday's sun. In full form, all of the guests seemed to be out and about, enjoying themselves. I watched each person for a few moments before watching another. As I viewed the guests, I noticed the women were well cared for by the men that stood by their sides. Even from afar, I could see how gorgeous the day dresses they wore were. The dresses had long, swishing bottoms made of the most elaborate material I'd ever seen. Several of the ladies complimented their dress and accessories with large, rimmed sunbonnets. Others also wore a matching ruffled, rimmed parasol.

I was a bit nervous while I waited to see the number of calling cards Laverne would return with. So, I began to count heads. There were a total of eighty-five guests. My forehead broke out in sweat. The day promised to be a scorcher. Silently, I professed about not being adjusted to this climate. I wondered what the rest of the summer would be like if it was already this hot in June.

My tent's covering was not unlike the others. It was covered on the top and back allowing a view on the three sides. The difference between my tent and the others was were it had been placed. There was quite a distance between my canopy and the others. My tent was set up on the left side of the house. This was where the lawn gave way to dense undergrowth. The heads of magnificent, old, oak trees were high in the sky. Their armed branches, filled with leaves, created their own canopy of shade.

The idea in being placed alone was to create complete privacy during the readings. Now, I was feeling a little vulnerable being so far away from the others. Everyone in attendance was family or friends and I felt silly acting this way. No matter how I tried consoling myself, I felt uneasy. Something about being here, about the dense foliage underneath the old oak tree was making me feel this way. At that moment, I looked up and saw Laverne walking toward me with the basket of calling cards in her hand.

The basket was filled with gray calling cards; all of the lettering had been printed with a gold pen. These classy calling cards had promised a long afternoon for Laverne and I. It took the better part of an hour to place the calling cards in numeric order and fill each into the appointment book. Each appointment was allotted thirty minutes. I was surprised when I saw several of the single men's calling cards. It would be interesting doing their readings and to see how accurate my observances from last night had been.

The rest of the afternoon flew by me. I hardly noticed each of the people that sat in front of me. As I did the readings, my mind was far into the futures of those who had come to see me. Hours after beginning, Laverne demanded I take half an hour to rest. She went to get a plate of food for me as I made my way to the house.

Nearing the house, I saw that most of the guests were taking their leave. Each hugged and thanked the host and hostess, proclaiming they'd had a wonderful time. Paul was standing in the circle driveway, wishing a safe trip home to those leaving. I was headed to the outside balcony that lead up to my room. As I passed him, Ella, the beautiful blonde-haired woman, was speaking to him. I heard her say, "I simply had a wonderful time. Darling, everything was superb as it usually is. The woman who read the cards is very good. I hope everything goes as planned. You know, she's very pretty with all of that red hair. If I were you, I wouldn't let her out of my sight." To my surprise, Paul replied, "Oh, I don't intend to." Suddenly, I felt like I was an eavesdropper. I rushed up the stairway as fast as I could.

Inside of my room, I couldn't help wondering what the under-current of that conversation meant. All at once, I became too tired to care. I needed to feel the comfort of my room. A nap was long overdue. The majority of the guests were gone, leaving the house very quiet and allowing me to immediately fall asleep.

Abruptly, I awoke and looked at my watch. Realizing that I'd been asleep for over two hours and dinner would soon be served, I started to reach for the cord, hanging beside the bed. When pulled, the cord called for a maid to come and attend; I needed to prepare myself for dinner.

Just as my hand was about to pull the cord, I heard a heated conversation between two men going on. Their voices were coming from the balcony outside of my room but they were standing on the other side, squarely in front of Laverne's bedroom. I wondered if Laverne could overhear their conversation. Softly, I got up from the bed and shut the French doors. Then, I quietly walked through the hallway, to Laverne's door. I delicately knocked on the door. After waiting a few moments, Laverne had not answered so I slipped into her room and shut the door. I tip toed to the French doors and put my ear up to them.

As I listened, I identified one of the voices as Paul's. I didn't recognize the other man's voice. As their conversation was nearing its end, I was able to hear the last few sentences. Paul said, "I'm warning you, I want this to go exactly as it was planned. I repeat – don't you dare put so much as a bruise on her body."

My heart stood still. What were they taking about? Who was she? Could they possibly be referring to me? I strained my ear to clearly hear what they were saying but I heard nothing. They were going to the stairway that led to the verandah and onto the circle driveway. I knew following them was useless as they'd be gone before I could get to the bottom of the stairway. I walked back to my room on the balcony and pulled the cord for the maid.

She immediately came into my room. She went to the chiffarobe and chose a yellow gown with matching yellow slippers for my evening attire. Many petticoats were needed to fill the skirt of the yellow gown. After what I had just heard, my body was very cold and the extra material would help in keeping me warm throughout the evening.

I dreaded having to face Paul. After what he had said, I never wanted to set my eyes on him, again. I wanted to tell Laverne that arrangements for our trip back to New York needed to be made as soon as possible. I wanted the safety that existed inside of our home. However, I'd given up on ever finding her alone.

Upon my entrance in the sitting room, I wasn't surprised when I saw Laverne's absence. Paul was the only person in the room and as he saw my entrance, he rose from his chair. Strolling over to me, he took my hand and kissed the palm. I jerked my hand from his. Paul was dumbfounded by my action but acted as if it didn't matter to him. Paul escorted me into the large chair that sat beside his. I preferred sitting, as well as, staying as far away from him as I could.

But, getting up would have been ungracious. Instead, I asked where everyone else was. His answer was shocking. "Everyone went into town for the evening." "Who is everybody?" I asked. Paul smiled as he replied, "Don't be alarmed. After all of today's happenings, Martha has retired upstairs in her rooms and is taking her dinner up there." I stood up and as I walked away, I said, "That sounds like a wonderful idea. I think that I will do likewise." With that, I began towards my room; Paul was out of his chair and standing in front of me in only two strides. He said, "I think not. The cook has already prepared a table for two on the outer terrace. She is probably dishing the food as we speak. Shall we go?"

I felt trapped and uneasy throughout dinner. But, I have to admit the food was delicious. We were served stuffed sole on a bed of wild rice with almonds topped with a creamy sauce. Paul insisted that I have a glass of white wine with dinner and when I finished the last drop, I could feel it had relaxed me, a little. During the course of dessert and coffee, I asked where Laverne was. I was furious with her for not telling me where she was going. Especially since she had professed the danger that this trip may bring. Being here, she had just thrown good sense and all caution to the wind. Trasping off to God only knows with the red-haired man named Bill. It would serve her right to meet trouble – head on because she was certainly asking for it.

The evening sped by. I found myself enjoying it much more than I cared to admit. Somewhere, inside the house, a grandfather clock chimed the hour of midnight. Paul, playing the perfect host, insisted on walking me upstairs to my bedroom. He left me at my door and started down the hallway, to the back of the house where his room was located. Not long after I'd climbed into my bed, I heard Laverne's footsteps making their way to her bedroom. She was safe and sound and I fell to sleep. Throughout the night, I was positive I heard planes overhead. What would a plane be doing in this part of the country? I fully intended on asking Paul about this in the morning. With that thought, I dozed off sleeping better than I had in months.

The dawn of the new day would change Laverne and my life, forever. The plan for the day was to have Paul, Bill, Martha and John show us the neighboring, adjoining estates. I hoped to see some of the areas that the Civil War was fought on. Our history was filled so much by the Civil War and Virginia and I was excited to see and learn some of it. But, sometime during the night, a storm had flown in.

By morning, dark clouds hung low in the sky. The thunder and lightening became closer and closer. Before the rain had started to fall, the air was filled with the smell of rain. When the first drops hit the edge of the balcony, I was standing in their path. Before I was able to reach my room, the rain began pouring heavily. In all of my life, I'd never seen it rain like this. Sometimes, when plans are made ahead and the rain comes interrupting those plans, all that can be said is Amen and I felt that this was one of those times.

Just as I was leaving my room, Paul was coming down the long corridor from his. We saw each other at the same time. The smile that appeared entirely lit up Paul's face. "Good morning," he said, "or should I say not so good?" "I think the latter phrase is much more appropriate," I replied. There was laughter in his voice as he said that I didn't sound as if I were in a very good mood. "Oh no, I am not in a bad mood, Paul. I've always believed that there is a reason for everything." Paul patted my arm, "Good girl. All's not lost; we can still tour the countryside in the enclosed car. We'll just have to make a few changes and the day will be as good as new!"

True to Paul's word, we did have an outing of sorts. He drove the four of us to a mansion that had been converted into an Inn. At the Inn, lunch and dinner were served. Laverne and I ate heartily. The food was excellent.

I'd never seen Laverne so full of life. If I didn't know better, I would have sworn she had fallen in love with Bill. She looked absolutely radiant. Paul was very attentive to me but for a while, I was not exceedingly friendly to either of the men. It seemed that everyone else was having such a good time. I finally resolve myself and started to have a wonderful time. Both men excused themselves, stating they needed a smoke to finish off the meal. Moments later, they were walking through the open doors. I could see the terrace from where I was sitting. Wrought iron tables and chairs were spaced some distance apart. If the weather had been agreeable, the terrace would have been a perfect place to have lunch. It was at this time that I noticed the rain had stopped and the sun was brightly shining.

I sat there a few minutes just thinking to myself. Paul didn't smoke, I'd stake my life on it. Laverne was staring at the open door that Bill had disappeared through. I startled her when I asked, "Does Bill smoke?" "No," she said, "I've not seen either of them smoking before. Why should you ask?" "It doesn't matter Laverne, don't worry about it – I was just wondering." I didn't want to spoil her day so I immediately dropped the subject. After a few more minutes of small conversation I excused myself, stating that I needed to use the powder room. Laverne hardly noticed as I left the room because her eyes were once again fixed upon the open doors that the men had made their exit through.

I looked around to see if anyone was watching me. I made my way through the open French doors, unnoticed by everyone. Once outside, I was on the terrace dining area and was pressing myself against the wall of the building. Many tall flowers filled the area, making it a perfect place to hide behind. Due to the recent rain, no one was yet dining on the open terrace. I looked around and could not see Paul or Bill anywhere. Where could they have gone in such a short period of time, I wondered. I was hidden behind one of the taller shrubs, which enabled me to take my time as I searched the entire area. There was a wide pathway, leading some distance away into the dense forest of trees. With no one in sight, I picked up the tail of my gray gown and swiftly walked to the pathway.

I trailed only a short distance down the path when the sound of mens' voices was dominant. I crept behind a large tree and began to listen. Paul was talking to two other men. I could see only the backs' of these other men but somehow these men were familiar to me. I'd seen these men before. I looked around for Bill but he was not in sight. Maybe, he'd gone back to sit with Laverne. I hoped so otherwise she would begin to wonder where I was. I crept closer and hid behind a second tree. Just as I was in place, the two men turned around, staring directly at the tree. I shrieked aloud when I saw their faces. I couldn't help myself; these were the same men that had followed me in New York.

Paul was the one responsible for these men; they were working for him. My face drained of all color. I had to get away from here now and Laverne had to come with me. Both of us were in grave danger. The two men had started toward the tree, which was hiding me. Throwing all caution to the wind, I ran out from behind the tree, making my way back to the Inn. I was running just as fast as I could but the long tail of my gown and the damp slippers on my feet were slowing my pace. I glanced back and saw the two men running in hot pursuit. Looking straight ahead, I tried running even faster. I did not go far because Paul was standing dead still in the pathway blocking my escape.

Inside of the Inn, Laverne had finally come out of her trance-like state of mind and realized I had been gone for a lengthy amount of time. As she glanced at her watch she realized that the men had been gone for over an hour. She stood up from the table, scanned the dining area and saw that only two couples remained. They were seated on the other side of the room. Laverne, intent on finding my whereabouts, started to walk to the front desk. Before she reached the desk clerk, she heard Bill calling her name. He had entered from the front of the building, just in time to keep Laverne from speaking with the clerk. Laverne was now walking over to Bill.

'No fool like an old fool' she chided at herself. It was time she came back to the real world. "Oh, there you are," she exclaimed, "Have you seen Joyce or Paul? They've been gone for an awfully long time." "As a matter of fact, I have," Bill, replied. "I'm sorry, I didn't have time to come and tell you. Paul took Joyce on the path leading from the terrace. This morning's rain made the path slippery and Joyce fell. I hate to be the bearer of bad tidings but she sprained her ankle. She's asking for you." "Where is she?" Laverne asked. "Has Paul taken her to a doctor? Is she going to be all right? Please take me to her, Bill." Laverne said – all in one breath.

Bill guided Laverne back through the dining area, out the open French doors, past the terrace and down the pathway, leading to the forest. Laverne, trying to keep up with Bill's long stride, found herself gasping for air. The pathway in front of her seemed to wind and twist in all directions. Laverne kept telling herself that surely they'd be there in a minute. Looking ahead, she saw a wooden bridge with wooden railings on the sides. Below the bridge was a creek, running swiftly.

Reaching the bridge, Laverne stopped and leaned against the bridge's railing. Bill walked past her stating, "Come on Laverne, its not much further until we are there." Laverne was surprised as they came upon a clearing in the forest. It looked to be some sort of deserted airfield. Weeds partially hid the runway. She saw a large, grayish-green cargo plane. Two men were standing beside the plane, as if they were waiting for someone to board before take-off.

In awe, Laverne looked at the plane. She had never seen a plane this close to her before. Bill had stepped behind

Laverne and quietly reached into the inner pocket of his suit. He brought out a small, brown box. Quickly, he opened the box and pulled out a cloth that reeked of ether. Laverne turned around towards Bill and he wrapped his arms around her. He placed a kiss upon her lips, murmuring, "Sorry my sweet, forgive me." Bill placed the cloth over Laverne's mouth and nose. Trusting Bill, Laverne had not struggled in Bill's arms. Now, her world was spinning and she felt herself slipping into darkness.

Within moments, the man standing by the plane had Laverne's limp form in his arms and was loading her onto the cargo plane. The men placed Laverne onto a mattress on the floor of the plane. They covered her body with a green, wool army blanket. Then, one of the men made his way to the cockpit. He was the pilot of this cargo plane and would be flying it momentarily. Bill was sitting beside the pilot and asked if his friend was okay. The pilot simply nodded his head, yes. The less we spoke, the better off we'd all be.

I just stood, staring at Paul. My shoulders were squared, my feet firmly planted on the ground and my head held high. If I was to go out of this world, I was going to do it with pride. Paul turned me in the direction of the two men. They stood very still on the forest's path; just waiting for Paul to give the last instructions. Paul pulled me toward him. With one arm around my waist, he whispered, "Trust me, if it had not rained this morning it would have been much simpler, my dear." Trust me, I thought. My arms were pinned to my sides but there was certainly nothing wrong with my feet. Slowly, I lifted my foot. With the heel of my shoe, I came down on his shoe just as hard as my little frame could. As he howled out, I felt a great deal of satisfaction – I'd hit home. Paul, in tremendous pain, motioned the co-pilot to come forward and help. Then, I felt a blow to my head. My ears rang and the rest of my senses had disappeared.

I knew that someone was carrying me. Trying to regain consciousness, I slowly opened my eyes. I saw a large cargo plane looming before me. We were only a few feet away from the side door, which was open. Paul was leading the way. He lifted himself up into the door's opening and was waiting for Benson, the man who was holding me, to lift me high enough so he could grab me and pull me through the doorway. "Be careful Ben, I don't want this woman to have so much as a bruise on her body," he warned. Ben murmured under his breath, "This woman has been nothing but a pain since the beginning. I'd like nothing more than squashing her. She's caused nothing but trouble from the start."

Paul pulled me into the plane. I hated him. He'd be sorry for doing this to me, I thought. I'll make his life miserable. Very carefully, Paul set me on the mattress lying in the middle of the plane's floor. I tried to get up off of the mattress and onto the floor so that I could crawl to the opening of the door. I found myself being dragged backwards by my heel. Kicking with my free foot, I made contact with flesh. However, my victory was short lived by Benson who flipped me onto my back and was dragging me back to the mattress.

Paul was kneeling at the head of the mattress. He had placed a pillow there for my head and was holding a white piece of cloth in his hand. My first thought was that Paul intended on tying me up and gagging me. Ben forced me down on the mattress and held my feet as Paul placed the cloth over my nose and mouth. The last thing I heard was the sound of the plane's engine turning over.

Paul took the seat nearest the rear of the plane. Benson, the pilot and his co-pilot took the two seats in front. The plane was airborne in a matter of seconds; headed to North Korea. Every few seconds, Paul found himself half turned in his seat looking back at Joyce to see if she was still out. He remembered the pain he felt when she'd driven her heel into the center of his foot. No doubt about it she was a spitfire and he knew it. Under different circumstances, he'd love the challenge he'd face trying to tame her.

The cargo plane landed in a remote area of North Korea. Part of the jungle had been cut down to make way for the secret airstrip. The government kept guards posted at the edges of the airstrip. There, in the jungle, were straw thatched huts for the guards to live in. A guard was posted twenty-four hours a day. The huts contained signaling devices that told the pilots when it was safe for the planes to land.

Paul knew that every second they remained at the airstrip brought more danger to all involved. So far, everything had gone as planned. Hurriedly, the men transported Joyce and her luggage to a car parked at the edge of the jungle. Both of us remained asleep. The car was black and had black shades that shut, allowing complete privacy for the occupants. Soon, with shades shut, the car was racing down a dirt road at break-neck speed. The cargo plane had landed early in the evening; by morning the car would be several hundreds of miles away. Then, and only then, would Paul breath easier. He began to rehash the situation to himself.

He hated involving the woman. But then, this woman wasn't just any sort of a woman – was she. The government needed her. Many, many secret agents had searched for the bombs in North Korea. All of their efforts were futile. Paul had gone on many of the fruitless missions. Not a single trace of the bombs could be found. If anyone would be able to find these bombs it was this lady, Joyce, with her supernatural powers.

She had written a letter to the president telling of the bombs' location. At first, the president had dismissed the woman and her letter. But, time was running out and he reviewed the letter once again. No one could have an imagination that was this good; she'd been so explicit and precise about every detail. She was worth a try.

The president had sent two secret service men to New York to check this woman out. Everything she stated about herself in the letter was true. Some of the comments she had predicted for the world had already taken place. The agents were very thorough in investigating Joyce's every move. She was well respected and highly thought of. She had gone to the poor in their need and often visited with the sick. Her foundation was solid and faultless.

Sometime during the course of the day, I awoke. I found myself laying full length across the seat in the back of the car. The car was moving at a very high rate of speed. I tried to sit up but waves of nausea came over me and caused me to lie back down. I drifted off to sleep; to sick to care about where I was being taken. Paul sat in the front seat of the car. He turned to look at my sleeping form and knew I was in need of food and water. But, he dare not risk stopping the car; we were traveling through dangerous territory.

Several hours later, the car turned off the main highway and continued down a dirt road, surrounded by the jungle. It had just rained and the road was slippery in spots; twice the car spun out of control. Ben with the strength of two other men was able to get the car back onto the road enabling our journey to continue. At last, Paul saw the long bamboo hut that sat high off of the ground on wooden stilts.

The hut was well built, much stronger than it appeared to be at first sight. The roof was made of bamboo branches. Lanterns lit the small driveway leading up to the hut. More lanterns appeared through the open windows of the house. A full-length porch with a straw roof ran the length of the house.

The rough ride in the car along the dirt road had fully awoke me. I stretched, raising my arms up and over my head. I felt so stiff; I didn't know if I would be able to make my way up the steps and onto the porch or let alone go into the house. There were several high backed bamboo chairs along the porch and I sank down, gratefully, into the first one I reached. My legs had kinks in them and walking was very painful. I could hear Paul conversing with someone inside; fluently speaking their language. A small Oriental woman came out onto the porch. She was carrying a large tray filled with small covered bowls of food. I opened the lid of each steaming bowl. The smell of food sent me scurrying down the steps, two at a time. I headed for the nearest tree, braced myself against it's trunk and started to heave.

I couldn't remember ever being this sick. I felt sure I was heaving my insides out. I was moaning so loud that I didn't hear Paul approaching me. I allowed Paul to lead me around to the back of the house. There was a covered well with a bench surrounding all of it's sides. Tubs to wash in were provided by the well. It sides were open and the roof was made of straw. Four large bamboo poles held up the roof.

Paul motioned for me to sit down on the bench. He walked over to the well and picked up a washpan filled with water. Towels had all ready been laid across the bench, beside me. Paul washed my face and hands, without saying a word. When the job was done, he led me back to the porch. Back to the chair where the tray of food had been placed. The tray had been removed and as I sat down the Oriental woman appeared again. This time, she had a smaller tray in her hands. It's contents consisted of plain tea and a steaming bowl of white rice. This simple meal settled my stomach and I began to feel much better.

The sleeping arrangements left a lot to be desired. I was shown to a cot at the far end of the building. Only a petition that went half way up separated my bed from the others. Paul moved his cot right up against the petition of mine. He felt awful that I'd been so sick earlier in the evening. If I was to need someone during the night he had decided he would be right there for me.

The car sped away in the blackness of the following night. We were going on the last lap of our journey.

The Bungalow

It was around three o'clock in the morning when we arrived at the Bungalow. In the darkness, I could barely make out the building. From what I could see, the building was very long. The outer walls were built of what looked to be sandstone. The heels of my shoes were clicking on some kind of stone possibly a stone pathway.

I was taken to the rear of the building. A small built woman with dark hair and brooding eyes stood in an open doorway, holding a lamp in her hand to light our way. Paul guided me past the woman and into a very large, long room. I noticed that there were small out coves in the room as well as chairs and couches grouped together in small sitting areas. Along the other wall were several closed doors; in all, they amounted to fifteen. Paul turned his back to me and began to speak with the small, dark haired woman. I was left standing in the middle of the room. Even at such a close distance, I could not make out what they were saying. This infuriated me. I started walking to the door, which I'd recently entered. I did not want to be in this strange place to begin with. I most certainly would not stand around, being ignored.

Out of the corner of Paul's eye, he saw Joyce walking right past him, headed for the door. Damn that woman. Couldn't she stand still for one single moment?

Paul took one long stride in my direction and with the voice of authority demanded I stop right there. I could hear the dark haired woman laughing. I decided that this was the last straw. I bolted straight toward the door. Paul caught up with me and swung me around in front of him. He shook me as he said, "Don't you ever try to run away from me again!" I was so angry with this man that I slapped him across the face. I declared, "Don't you ever talk to me in that tone of voice again and keep your filthy hands off of me!"

For a moment, Paul was stunned. He stood in total disbelief, as a woman had never struck him before. He touched his cheek; it still stung from the blow. Kitty, the dark haired woman, walked over to Paul. She smirked as she said; "You've got your hands full with that one. I'm off to bed. You take care of the Little Princess. I've got work to do tomorrow."

One by one, all of the brown doors had opened. Sixteen women in all were craning their heads around the doors of their rooms. They were trying to see what all of the fighting was about but with one look from Kitty each door was quietly shut. I was fuming; with everything that had previously happened to me and I had to have an audience for this last scenario. In all of my life I had never struck anyone, until now. I began to tremble and the tears that had been held back through everything else rolled down my cheek. Sobbing was the only thing I could do because I felt like I had lost all control.

As Paul silently pondered the events of the past days he thought: this has got to be the most complex woman on earth. Her sobs are real and in all truth, she has gone through a lot. If I were a woman instead of a man, I might be crying myself. So, Paul held her in his arms and softly spoke the most comforting words he could think of. When her sobbing had ceased, he took her arm and led her down the long room, through the outer alcove and they stopped at the front of the brown door.

Somewhat regaining my composure, I asked Paul why he'd brought me to this God forsaken place. And, while I was at it; I asked, "Who is the dark haired woman that resembles a harlot?" With my description of Kitty, Paul asked me why I thought of her in that way. With my spunk returning, I replied, "Well, for Heaven's sake – why wouldn't I think it of her? Her nightgown falling so low that her pumped up tits practically fall out and in plain view." Paul couldn't help but laugh. It was true; Kitty did look like a harlot but it was her job to look like one.

Paul turned the key in it's lock and opened the door wide for my entry. I walked into the room and sat down on the white satin bedspread. Thinking of how I hated white; I asked Paul, "Why did you bring me here? I need to know. Who was that woman and what was her name?" Paul looked at me with a serious face as he sat down into the rattan chair that was placed closest to the bed. He said, "Her name is Kitty. No one here is as they might appear to be. Be careful – your life will depend on it." Paul stood up; he was ready to leave after these last words of warning, "Trust Kitty and no one else. I repeat, no one. Now, I've got a long way to travel and will explain more when I return." He walked to the door, opened and closed it behind him and turned the key in the lock. As he walked away, Paul thought of how nice it would be to sleep for a solid week. Never, he thought had he been so completely exhausted as he felt now. I was so exhausted myself that I fell across the bed, still wearing the gown from the day. I was asleep before my head had hit the pillow.

Laverne had been treated in much the same way as Joyce had been. She flew in her own cargo plane which landed at the same airfield as Joyce's plane had. There, a car was waiting to take the passengers to their final destination. She had been at the place called the Bungalow for three days. She had to take a flight of stairs to reach her room, which was located at the far end of the large room. Her room was large and spacious with one window that had bars on the outside. Laverne had no complaints about her room. However, she did mind being locked up inside of it. There was a maid, who in slack time would come and go. The maid served Laverne two meals a day. She ate her meals at the wicker table set that was placed by the barred window. There was a small sitting area and book shelves on the other side of the window.

The bars on the window depressed Laverne. On the fifth day, she began to feel like a caged animal. She paced herself around the floor and ate little to none of the food the maid brought. In the evening, Laverne could hear laughter, which came from both males and females. It seemed to come from some sort of gathering place and music was being played in its background. She was lonely and missed her companion, Joyce. She also missed Bill. She wondered how she could have been foolish enough to fall for him. All of his sweet-talking had merely been done to lure her to the plane; which had taken her so far away from Joyce. If she got her hands on him again, she'd claw his eyes out.

The next day, as she sat in one of the chairs near the window, she saw that her wish might indeed come true. Below her, Bill was walking across the compound. The compound was completely covered by sand colored stones and as far as she could see, surrounded by an eight-foot wall. During the day, Laverne had been observing what happened in the compound. There was a long row of buildings and women went back and forth from them. The most puzzling thing about these women was that each had a certain color of clothing to wear and day after day, they each wore the same color. Some wore nothing but brown. Others wore only yellow, blue, light green or dark green. As she realized this, she went to her closet to take a second look at her apparel. She pulled out the few long dresses that were inside and laid them on the bed. Each dress was lavender. Not only the dresses were lavender but also her nightgown and her petticoats. She wondered why she had not realized this before. She knew that each color must have some sort of symbolic meaning but what was the meaning?

The only contact outside that Laverne had was with the maid. The maid was an Oriental woman, late in her years and didn't speak a word of English. Each day, the maid brought the food into the room, placed it on the table, bowed to Laverne and then walked out of the room, locking the door behind her. Laverne had told the maid several times that she had to get out of here. But, it was to no avail; all Laverne received for her effort was a puzzled look and a reply spoke in a foreign language. How could she possibly find out what was going on? The only thing that she felt sure of was that if Bill was here earlier, than he would be back. An idea began to form in her head. Laverne decided that she would sit at the window and write down what she saw and the time she had seen it.

Throughout the course of the next week, she gathered more information than she realized and by taking some sort of action, she felt better mentally. By the end of each day, she was worn out and found that she was sleeping much better than she had in the past. She'd also begun to eat her meals.

Every day, Laverne observed the women, most of them young, come and go. They were always dressed in the color that had been selected for them. On a day toward the end of the week, she noticed something different about the pattern of women coming and going. The blonde haired woman that always wore a long, blue dress and a white bib apron was different today. She seemed much taller and the dress that always went down to her ankles was about four inches above the ankles. Also, her hair looked darker. Could it be someone else wearing the blonde woman's clothing?

At six o'clock in the evening, all of the women would leave the row of buildings and return to the Bungalow. Laverne sat close to the window this evening. As they returned, she studied each of them like a hawk. The woman who was always dressed in blue had not returned. Curious, Laverne waited and waited.

An hour later, the older Oriental woman who served her each meal, stood outside, talking to a man who was dressed in a Korean uniform. Their conversation lasted fifteen minutes. Laverne wondered where the man in the military attire had come from. And, what was he doing talking to someone as old as the Oriental woman?

To her surprise, the guard entered the long building that the women worked inside of, through the main door. A few minutes later, the woman that had appeared taller this morning, came out of the building. She was dressed in blue and her hands were tied behind her back. What had she done to deserve this? Had she stumbled upon something that shed some light on why she was here?

The next morning, the older Oriental woman delivered Laverne's breakfast tray. As she set the food down, she noticed the notes. Laverne quickly placed her napkin over them and gave the woman a friendly smile. The woman was all ready on her way out of the room. As she reached for the doorknob she turned her head in Laverne's direction. Her eyes had become mere slits and she wore a face that was anything but friendly. In broken English, she said, "I under estimated you, my dear. Something will have to be done about this!" Her tiny frame went through the doorway and she shut the door, softly. Laverne was standing clear across the room but could still hear the door as it was locked.

She had been anticipating the food's arrival for a while because she was quite hungry. But now, her heart was in her throat and she found that she could not take a bite. Her entire body was shaking. Every instinct that she had ever felt was now screaming "WARNING" and this warning was felt throughout.

She had to dispose of her notes. But, how could she? There was no place to hide anything in this damn room. She could burn the papers if she had matches; she didn't. If she tore them up and threw them into the wicker wastebasket, the papers would easily be placed back together. She had to dispose of them; it was her safety that was based on this task.

Three hours later, her prayers were answered. She had been sitting near the window since the maid had left that morning. As she looked down into the compound she saw Bill. His flaming red hair could not have gone unnoticed. He was taking his time, walking across the compound. He had stopped and was now directly under Laverne's barred window.

Without hesitation, Laverne snatched one of the books from the shelf. She securely placed her notes inside of the leather bound book, slipping them between several of it's pages. She ran back to the window and sighed in relief because Bill was still beneath her. He stood in the same place as if he were waiting to receive something. And, that he did; Laverne slipped the book through the bars of the window and watched as it bounced off of Bill's shoulder and fell only six inches from his feet. Bill bent over and picked the book up. He looked up at the building and could see the upper portion of Laverne's body. He could see that she was dressed in pale lavender.

Laverne was saying only one word and it was danger. But, the distance between the couple was too great and Bill tried but could not comprehend her message. He shook his head sideways until Laverne understood what he meant. She left the barred window, momentarily. When she returned she held a sheet of paper up to the window; it read: danger. Had she been closer, Laverne would have seen all of the color in Bill's face drain. Bill nodded his head to Laverne silently saying, "Yes, I understand." Then, with the book in his hand, he swiftly walked to his car and drove off as if the devil had been after him. His windows were rolled down and his red hair was standing straight on the top of his head. He was driving at a high rate of speed. Only when he saw the dirt road that reared off to the right, did his speed slow. The car came to a complete halt.

Bill grabbed the book and shook it upside down. One by one, the papers fell onto the passenger seat. Bill read and re-read the information that Laverne had given him. This was the break that he and Paul needed; the one that he had been hoping for. The one that had put Laverne in extreme danger.

Turning the key over, Bill started the motor. The old, black Ford had seen it's better days. The black paint had begun to fade and these spots were covered in brown rust. The car and the condition it was in had allowed Bill to travel some dangerous roads. Some of these, Paul had even refused to drive on; it was too risky.

Bill could see the image of Laverne's face; it was terror-stricken. Somehow, he had to get her away from the compound and into a much safer place. With this picture planted in his head, Bill was back on the highway; once again, driving at a high speed. The car's shocks were shot and caused the car to swerve from the right side of the road to the left. Bill paid no attention to the swaying of the car. Although, he did become concerned when the car began to overheat because he was driving at such a high speed. As the car rolled into the gravel driveway of Paul's estate, black exhaust smoke bellowed out from the rear of the car.

Looking at his watch, Bill saw that it was eleven-thirty at night. He knew Paul would not be fond of this situation. At this point, Bill was past caring about anything besides Laverne's safety.

That night, Paul and Bill spent over three hours discussing the danger that Laverne was in. The information that she had managed to attain put them one step closer to solving the ongoing problem of the women agents that were vanishing. As they completed the final stages of Laverne's rescue, the Grandfather clock struck four-thirty. It was early in the morning and they'd decided that Laverne would be rescued tonight, just before dawn.

More than ten days had passed and there had been no word from Paul. I spent most of my time pacing the floor in one of my long, white skirts. This morning, the long sleeved white blouse with the high collar was too tight at my throat. There was little comfort to be received here and I was far beyond caring about my appearance; so, I simply ripped the collar open.

It was very clear to me that I had to get myself out of this room, out of this isolation. As I looked around the room, searching for help, my eyes fell to the window that was just below the ceiling. The length of the window looked to be about thirty-six inches and the width was somewhere around two feet. Hmm, I thought; was this going to be possible? With the table beneath the window, I could reach the sill. But, did I have enough strength in my arms to raise my body up and through the open window? This was the only chance that I had, at this time, to escape. I absolutely had to try.

During the past few days, I'd felt that Laverne's presence was very near to mine. She may even be inside one of the closed doors that I'd seen when I arrived. If so, it was probable that she was also locked up; being held in the same way I was – as a prisoner.

If my chance arose, I would strangle Paul with my bare hands. Neither Laverne or I had ever done anything to warrant this kind of treatment. Where did he get off, thinking he could treat me this way? I was becoming livid with this situation. The room was not only hot but also humid. I hated this climate and I hated the room even more.

Rarely, was I able to fall asleep before one o'clock in the morning. Every night at eight o'clock, the piano music began. The gayness and laughter of both men and women went along with the music. This would just go on and on, lasting hours. Last night, a horrible thought had come into my mind. What if Paul had placed me into a house of prostitution? What was I to do? Even the remote chance of this becoming my reality had caused me to throw myself into the middle of the bed, uncontrollably sobbing.

This morning I felt almost entirely recovered from the frustration and depression that had overcome me earlier. It seemed that my tears from the previous evening had released a lot of the tension and the fear that had been building up inside of me for so long. The shedding of tears had cleansed my body, mind, and soul.

I sat down and calmly began to plan out my escape. Minutes later, Dee (the young woman who brought my meals to me) came in to serve lunch. Dee spoke a small amount of very broken English. In a way, we had become friends.

I was perfectly calm as I watched her enter the room. I was even able to ask in a nonchalant manner, "What do you say about me walking around the grounds? You can come with me." Dee looked at me for a moment with a sorrowful face and sad eyes. Her gaze fell to the floor and with her head held down, she walked to the door. "I try misses. I try." she said. With that, she rushed through the door and quickly fastening the lock.

As dusk was about to come that evening, I heard a knock on my door. I listened as the key turned in the lock. The door opened and there, in front of my eyes was Paul. So stunned by this sight, I gasped aloud; I'd given up on Paul ever returning for me. To my surprise, his tall frame was filling the doorway, dressed in a North Korean uniform.

Softly, he said, "Before you start yelling at me, let me explain." I knew as the words came out of my mouth they'd be regretted. Seeing him, brazingly standing there in a uniform that belonged to another country made me so angry that I was not able to hold my tongue. I yelled, "You are nothing but a liar and a traitor and a disgrace to your country. Don't you dare come one step closer to me – if you do I'll scratch your eyes out. Get out of this room, out of my sight! For as long as I live, I don't want to ever see you again!"

Paul replied, "That my dear, may be a very short time if you don't calm yourself down and let me explain." I yelled my response to him, "Get out or I'll start screaming so loud that all of your little sluts will hear me as they slink themselves around during the day. They just wait for the night to fall so that they can display themselves; no doubt, with the same neck line as your precious Kitty flaunts herself in."

In a rage, Paul stomped through the room and over to the closet. He threw the closet door open and examined each of the white gowns. The dress that Paul yanked from the closet had the lowest neckline I'd ever seen. After throwing it across the bed, he stated, "Be ready, tonight, at eight o'clock sharp in this gown. If you're not, I'll enjoy the pleasure of dressing you in it!" "Oh, no you won't", I yelled, "You'll keep your hands off of me!" Paul turned his back to me and walked to the door. "You'd better be wearing this gown or you'll live to regret it!" he warned and then he walked out, slamming the door behind him.

Paul had come back to the Bungalow trying to get the word to Laverne that she would be rescued two days hence, right before dawn. He was furious with Joyce. She never let him get a word in edgewise, not even for a second. Never, in all of his life had he met a woman that could infuriate him yet excite him in the manner that she could. She was a red headed hellion, so demure on the surface but underneath a hellion lived. That woman needed to be tamed; Paul felt he was the right man for the job.

With Kitty's help, Paul was allowed to see Laverne. He informed her of the plans made to rescue her. She expressed how very grateful she was to him, more than once. It was no wonder, Paul thought, that Bill cared for Laverne. She was so genuinely sweet and kind, eager to help in any way she could. It was too bad that Joyce had not let some of Laverne's kindness and gratitude rub off on her. Joyce should've been glad to see him. He had kept his word by finally returning. Instead, she'd stomped her small feet while moving her arms in all directions to indicate her displeasure with his return.

It was seven-thirty that night, by the time he'd finished his business with Laverne and conferred with Kitty. In my room, I was dressing myself. I knew that Paul meant what he said: if I wasn't in the dress than he would put me into it. Fine, I thought. Oh, I'll be dressed all right and he'll be wishing he were dead before the evening is over!

These thoughts consoled me as I slipped the long, layered, white silk gown over my head and cinched in my waist as tight as I could. I would simply ignore Paul throughout the entire evening; spending my time flirting with all of the other men. I had also decided to find out where each of the doors lead. Before this night was over, I was going to escape; leaving that despicable man behind me, forever.

At eight o'clock, straight up, Paul knocked on Joyce's door. He expected that she was not going to be dressed. He was going to enjoy this fight; dressing her in the gown he'd chosen earlier. He was going to cherish every moment it took to bring her under his will. He'd come prepared with a clean, white handkerchief to gag her, if need be. There was a grin on his face as he unlocked the door and walked into the room. Paul stopped dead in his tracks because Joyce was fully dressed and completely ready with her red hair piled high on her head and her waist all cinched in. This was the most beautiful creature he'd eve seen and for a moment, he stood in place, speechless as he took in her beauty.

As I looked into Paul's eyes, I could see his desire for me. For once, saying nothing pleased me. I had never seen a man look at me like this before. Paul held eye contact with me during our brief moment of silence. Eventually, he cleared his throat and said, "Well, I see that for once, you were able to do as you were told to. If my need to be free of this room and inspect my surroundings had not been so urgent, I would have slammed the door in his face and locked it myself!

I took everything in, not missing a single detail, as I was lead into the long room by Paul. I noticed the windows, doors, alcoves and the most important factor, the men and women occupying these spaces. The moment that I walked into the main area of the room I felt all of the eyes on me. Every single person had turned their head toward me and I could hear gasps of surprise coming from the ones standing closest to me. As I glanced across the room (still observing every detail) my eyes locked with a tall, dark man that was standing near the open double doors. He had the darkest and most penetrating eyes that I had ever seen. His origin appeared to be half American and half Japanese.

Paul was standing beside Joyce. As he saw the looks exchanged between the two, he felt his heart sink. The man Joyce was gazing at was definitely the most dangerous man in the room. Power, wealth and Japan were all on this man's side; supporting his pedestal of danger. Several weeks ago, Paul had been introduced to him; his name was Lee Yeng. With his knowledge of Mr. Yeng, Paul began to silently prayer that the red haired vixen standing beside him would not betray him.

Paul steered me toward the long table that had been set up as the bar. One end of the table held assorted liquors, mixes and wine. Small dishes of hot food sat on the other end. The Oriental dishes had matching cups. They'd been designed with orange poppies as the designing flower, set on a wheat colored background.

I let Paul guide me over to the assorted dishes of food which all smelled delicious. I had spent the last two hours preparing myself for the evening and had not eaten anything since morning. I could not wait to fill my plate with food and enjoy the taste of the food that smelled so good.

Every moment spent in this room courted danger and Paul was very aware of this. He wondered why he'd insisted Joyce accompany him; he wished she were not here. There were far too many soldiers, both North Korean and Japanese, staring at her with their mouths open in admiration. It seemed that whenever he and Joyce were together, trouble was never far behind.

Paul steered me toward the double open doors that led onto a large, stoned terrace. Tables and chairs had been set up on the terrace allowing the guests to also enjoy the evening's warm, fresh air. A few couples were all ready seated outside.

Paul needed to breathe the open air. He needed to find a discreet table, set away from the other couples, to dine at. After they ate, he could say the things that needed to be said; they could talk. Both of them were in grave danger by being in this particular compound. He knew that Joyce needed to be warned, as soon as possible.

As I was led through the doors, I noticed the handsome Japanese/American man standing beside the door. In one of his hands was a drink and in the other was a lit cigarette. As I passed him, he put his cigarette out, strolled to the middle of the path and stopped. He stood in front of Paul and me, blocking our progress. Swearing under his breath, all Paul could think was 'let the dual of wits began'. Lee Yeng stood six inches shorter than Paul and this, surprisingly, made Paul feel better.

Lee and Paul spoke in Japanese for a few minutes. Yeng spoke rapidly and the tone of his voice rose and then lowered in a matter of seconds. I stepped to the side of the men when their conversation began. Paul had handed me his plate, which was piled high with food. As I stood there waiting, with both of our plates in my hands, I realized that they were quite heavy. I began to walk away from the men to a table when the men began to converse in English. I was formally introduced to Mr. Yeng, whom referred to himself as Lee. His eyes never left mine, even as he bowed during our introduction.

Out of courtesy, Paul asked Yeng to join us at our table. To Paul's regret, the man smiled at Joyce and accepted the offer. There was nothing like dining with the enemy at your table. The battle of wits began. Every time that I raised my eyes from my plate, the man that was speaking to Paul was staring at me. I hated people scrutinizing me, especially while I was eating. I took a few more bites before I set my fork down and pushed the plate away from me. As I did, Yeng got up from the table, walked over to my chair and asked me for my first dance. I had been oblivious to the fact that most of the couples had vacated the tables and begun to dance. For the first time in days, I had not even heard the music that played each evening. I noticed that tonight, the music being played was soft and had a romantic melody to it.

Furious, Paul slammed his napkin down as he rose from the table. Yeng had taken Joyce from him in a single swoop. Each time Paul neared the dancing couple, Yeng lead Joyce in the opposite direction. The split second that the music stopped, Paul began to march towards them.

The hour was late and the evening a dismal failure. Paul's patience was at the end of its rope. As he pulled me away from Yeng's side, he said, "I believe you have something that belongs to me." Yeng was angry and started to reply but thought better of it. He walked out of the room with his head held high and his back straight. In a dangerous mood, he left the building and walked to his car, where the chauffeur stood, waiting.

Yeng was accustomed to having his way. He was going to have this woman with glossy blue/black eyes and flaming red hair, even if he had to kill for her. When he arrived at his house, he had the butler fix him a stiff drink. He stood on the second story balcony, looking into space. Yeng had already begun to plan how he would get this woman that had stolen his heart. Tomorrow, he was going back to the bungalow with a picnic basket in his hand. He would drive her to the countryside for lunch and she would not be returning to the Bungalow. Then, and only then, she would be completely his.

Paul was not a very good dancer. He struggled through the last dance with me. The curfew hour of one o'clock was upon the men and this included Paul. Unfortunately, what he had to say was going to have to wait. He led me through the long room and to the alcove that was just outside of my room. He kissed me on the forehead, turned around on his heel and said, "Trust no one and particularly Yeng. He is a mean and dangerous man." With that he was gone.

I was not used to being out of my room and I felt very tired. Sleep came easily to me. In the deepest hour of sleep, I began to dream. I dreamed of a dark, handsome man, standing in uniform next to a car that was parked in an open field. The jungle had been cleared away and I could see that the man's hair was blowing in the gentle breeze. I could see that he had a picnic basket in his hand but I could not make out whom the man in the distance was. As I walked closer, I recognized that this dark, handsome man was Yeng.

The breeze blew my high-necked, lacy white dress behind me as I walked toward him. I didn't notice that it left part of my ankles showing because all I could see and think of was Yeng. He reached out, taking my hand and we walked to the edge of the jungle. Here, in the dense shade he laid a blanket on the ground and set the picnic basket on top of it. Just as we were comfortably seated, the chauffeur walked over to us. He was bringing a chilled bottle of champagne, which he poured, into two long stemmed, crystal glasses. He left after handing us each a glass that was filled to the rim.

It was a beautiful afternoon. Yeng had seen to every last detail himself. The place he'd chosen was beautiful, the food was delicious and the champagne was superb. The tropical heat always made me sleepy at this time of the afternoon. He offered me a pillow and I took his suggestion of laying down on the edge of the blanket. Yeng summoned for the chauffeur to come and take the remains of our lunch away. In pretense, Yeng stood up and said he needed to stretch. He told me to rest while he took a short walk. I was comfortable and asleep only moments after he left.

In my dream, three men in Japanese clothing came towards me. I awoke, hearing the men as they were approaching. My heart was in my throat. I got up and ran into the jungle just as fast as my legs would carry me. As I ran through the dense foliage, vines snagged on my clothing and ripped at my hair. More of the vines were on the ground and were tripping me as I ran. Finally, I could run no more. With each breath I took a loud gasp came from my throat. I sank to the ground, allowing to foliage to hide me from the view of the men that were hot on my trail. Seconds later, I heard their footsteps searching for me. I held my breath as they searched the area. Finally, convinced that I was not in this area, they left to search elsewhere.

When I awoke from the dream of the dream, I felt like all of my energy had been drained out my body. My mouth had an awful taste in it. I stumbled out of bed and over to the basin. I cleaned myself, splashing water on my face several times; hoping that it would refresh me. When that was done, I brushed my teeth and combed my hair. I walked back to bed, slipped down into the covers and waited for breakfast to arrive.

Late that afternoon, the Oriental maid came to tell me that I could see the grounds. I followed Dee into the long room and out onto the terrace where I had dined the night before. I followed her past the tables and benches, to the backside of the building. We walked out into the enclosed yard and then into the sand colored building that covered one side of the yard. Inside we walked through one office, through another and another. We stopped at the last door, which said 'Do Not Enter'. I wanted to know what was behind this door and decided I would have to come back when no one else was present.

As I looked around, I noticed that most of the women that had entertained the man from the night before were here, inside the building. They were working in the offices that contained high power equipment. Each seemed to be very efficient at what she did. Here, nothing was what it appeared to be on the surface. I began to understand why Paul had brought me here. He needed me to find out what was taking place here, what was going on right under these people's noses. This was something that he'd failed at.

I felt a chill and knew that my thoughts were right on the target. My first psychic intuition was hidden bombs, beneath the ground, were near-by. Goose bumps surfaced on my skin. I knew that somehow I had to find the underground passage that led to the bombs. I also had to get word to Paul. I felt much better knowing Paul was really on our country's side; not the enemies.

All night, I tossed and turned trying to picture that opened to the underground passage. A little before dawn, I dozed off. A few minutes later, I awoke and knew exactly where the door was located. How was I ever going to be able to go back to the offices and unlock that forbidden door? Somehow, I had to. Then, I thought maybe I could get my maid, Dee to start talking about herself and her family. Maybe, Dee had a lover; she was certainly pretty enough to have one.

When Dee entered the room I was all ready up and dressed for the day. She appeared with my breakfast tray in her hands and was surprised to see me dressed in a plain white gown. As Dee set the tray on the table she said, "Missy don't like my dress? You not pleased with me?" I saw a single tear escape from her beautiful black eyes and as I watched it slide down her cheek, I knew that I could not use this beautiful creature as a decoy. I also knew that this decision put me back at square one.

I was surprised because Dee did not seem to be in a hurry to leave my room. When she suggested to re-do my hair I allowed her to. This seemed to really please her. As I sat in front of the dressing table that held a small mirror, Dee said, "Place evil. Missy should leave this place. I no want you killed." I was stunned; my eyes were wide opened by her last two words. I asked, "Who would want to kill me?" She did not answer my question until she'd placed the last curl into its place. She lowered her voice to a whisper when she said, "Lee Yeng dangerous man. He like you. He take you on picnic – you tell him you're sick. He very bad man, take my sister and kill her when he done with her."

I held my breath for two reasons. Wondering how Dee knew of my dream, I asked, "How is it that you know I dreamed of this?" She said, "I not know you dream of it. I hear guards talking. Lee Yeng plan on taking you on picnic and after, kidnap you! He come next Wednesday." "Oh, Dee," I exclaimed, "Will you help me to escape from here before this can happen?" Dee replied, "Yes. O.K., where Missy go I go to."

I turned the stool I was sitting on, when she'd fixed my hair, around to hug her. Tears welled up in my eyes as I held her close to me. After six weeks of being held as a prisoner, God had answered my prayers. I had finally found someone I could trust!

We only had five days to get away from here. If only Paul would come back, I thought. It had been two weeks since I'd seen him last. I thought of Kitty. I had not seen her when I had visited the offices. What had become of her? In all of the time I'd been her, she didn't once send me word about anything. Was this woman as trustworthy as Paul had claimed she was? Soon, I would find my answer.

During the night, I heard someone at my door. Someone was fumbling with the lock but after a few seconds, I heard the key in the lock turn. Someone had just unlocked my door! I held my breath in, I knew whoever it was would come in any moment. When the door opened, I was able to tell it was the shadow of a lady. But, in the darkness, I could not make out who it was. The woman appeared too tall to be Dee. She steadily walked to my bed and stood, looking down at me. With the speed of lightening, her hand came down over my mouth. I started to struggle with her. She was a strong woman. She said, "You fool, stop struggling with me! I'm Kitty and you're in danger. I've got to get you out of here."

She released her hand from my mouth, allowing me to whisper, "Where's Paul?" Kitty replied, "Paul can not help you. His cover was blown the night you appeared with him at dinner. Lee Yeng had someone check out his record. He just barely escaped from being captured the night they rescued your friend." I asked, "What friend?" "Well," Kitty said, "the woman you came with. Your companion, of course. Who else would it be?"

Indeed, who else, so Laverne had been close to me this whole time. I felt better by knowing this but was even happier when I knew Paul had gotten her out of here and to safety. I took a deep breath and asked, "Kitty, do you know where the bombs are?" She replied, "No, I've never been able to find out. I'm watched too closely just as everyone else is. Paul always thought they were somewhere close." You're standing on top of them," I said. Kitty looked surprised. I continued to explain, "They are underground. I need your help finding them. Kitty, I need your key for the door that's locked, the one at the end of the offices."

Kitty took a moment before she said; "There's not time for that now. I've got to get you out of here, tonight. "No," I said, "I won't go until I know for sure that I'm right. I've got to make sure the bombs are below us. I can't leave." Kitty exclaimed, "Well, if you're not the most exasperating person I've ever met, I don't know who is. Okay, Okay, you have one hour to go and find your bombs. Whether you find them or not, you must be back here by one o'clock. Do you understand?" "Yes, Kitty," I said and promised her I would be back this morning by one, with or without the knowledge I was searching for. Then, I said, "Have Dee, my maid ready. She'll be leaving with me." "Well, I'll be darned," Kitty, replied, "I would have never guessed that she was one on our side. I'll have her ready. Remember, one hour is all you have." She handed me a string of keys and wished me luck.

I raced across the room, out the door and into the yard. I was headed straight for the office building when I stopped dead in my tracks, remembering the guards. I looked up; expecting to find a gun aimed for me but instead I saw the guard slumped over the railing. Instantly, I knew he was dead. Continuing my search, I found the key to unlock the outside door of the building. I was able to race through the offices because their doors were always kept unlocked. At last, I was at the locked, dead-bolted door. It took me a few minutes to find the correct key. Finally, I unlocked it. I stepped through the doorway but because of the darkness, I didn't see the stairs. I plunged; head first, down the entire flight.

I must have passed out from the pain but I didn't know for how long. Other than hurting like crazy I seemed all right. I cautiously raised my arm to look at my watch. I could not see the time because of the darkness. I held my wrist to my ear to see if it was even ticking. It wasn't; I'd broken it during the fall. I braced my back against the stonewall and managed to lift myself to a standing position. The pain on my right side was almost more than I could bear. I felt dizzy and nauseated but I willed the pain away. My eyes were becoming adjusted to the darkness and holding myself against the wall, I began walking down some kind of tunnel. Able to see more than I thought was humanly possible, I spotted the bombs! They were a dull greenish gray. The bombs were suspended on cement racks that went on for as far as my eyes I could see.

I'd seen all that I needed to see. I didn't dare stay any longer because I had no idea what time it was. My instincts led me back to the stairs. It was hard to see the steps in the dark. Concentrating on my feet, I tripped on my long, white gown and almost fell backwards. I shuddered at the thought of falling again. Three steps later, I re-entered the offices. I raced through each of them. I exited the building, ran across the yard and re-entered the Bungalow.

I made my way across the room but in the middle of it, I stumbled over something. I bent down and touched the object. It was a dead body; the flesh was still warm. The person had been shot in the back. I rolled the body over and saw that it was Kitty! She lay at my feet, dead. I strangled my sobs back as I ran back to my room. Upon reaching the door, I found it locked, from the inside. Kitty was dead so, how was this possible? Had she locked it before she was killed or was it locked after her death? If it had been locked afterwards, they'd be searching for me. I took the chance and softly knocked on the door. I was about to walk away when the door cracked open and there inside stood Dee. I don't think I'd ever been so glad to see a person, as I was when I saw her.

Once I was inside the room, I re-locked the door. I looked across the room at my nightstand. The clock read one twenty-five in the morning; I had not been here in time. Dee was sitting in the corner closet by the door. She was softly crying. I walked back to the door and unlocked it from the inside. As I turned the doorknob, nothing happened. It was then that I heard the bolt from the other side of the door slam shut. The door was our only way out.

Feeling defeated, I sat down on the edge of the bed. It was only a matter of time before I would be just as dead as Kitty was. My life and what it could have been flooded before my eyes. I would never see Paul again. I looked over at Dee and to my surprise she'd gained a bit of self control. She was staring at the window near the roof.

"It is no use, Dee. The windows are too high. Even if we could reach it, it would still be too narrow for our bodies to crawl through," I said. Disregarding what I'd said, Dee took a chair and placed it on the table that sat below the window. She climbed up onto the table and asked me to hand her the other chair. As I lifted it up, the weight caused unbearable pain in my chest and I had to set it down. Then, I thought of the pain that being shot, as Kitty had been, realizing that pain would be far worse, I managed to lift it up to her on the second try.

She stacked the second chair on the first one. She climbed up into the seat and balanced herself in it. After a moment, she stood up and reached for the window seal. To my amazement, she was able to lift her body into the narrow opening of the window. She pulled her body out of the window and dropped to the ground.

My rib stung like it was on fire. How on earth could I possibly accomplish what Dee had? I didn't have enough strength left to pull myself up and through that narrow opening. Unfortunately, it was the only choice that I had left. I climbed onto the first chair and then onto the second. So far, so good. I reached out to grip the window's seal but the pain in my ribs was so intense that I instantly let go and almost fell over backwards. On my second try, I held on tight. Sweat broke out on my forehead and for a second, I thought I was going to faint. I cried out, "Oh God, please help me!" I felt his power enter me and with this strength was able to push hard enough to get my upper body through the window. My legs were dangling inside of the window looking for something solid to push against. I was trying to see behind me as long arms reached up into the air and met my swinging arms. With one strong jerk from these arms, my body came tumbling through the window. I crashed down, nailing the owner of these arms to the ground. Just before I passed out from immense pain I heard Paul's voice say, "I knew you'd be glad to see me again but you didn't have to attack my body in order to prove it!"

Dee knew that her mistress was in pain and needed her help. She was trying to get me away from Paul and said, "Get off of her you ox! Can't you see she's hurt?" Paul looked up at the dark angry eyes of her beautiful Oriental face and feeling angry himself, replied, "Can't you see I'm trying to help her? What do you mean, she's hurt?" Dee said, "No time! They will soon come find us!" Paul said in a soothing voice, "Hold on, sweetheart. We've got one more passenger coming with us. We've just got to wait a little longer."

Bill stood in the shadows of the jungle, swearing under his breath that Paul was taking entirely too much time. Something had gone wrong, he thought. He walked steadily through the darkness until he saw Paul. He was working on a woman that lay on the ground and there was a little Oriental woman hovering near them.

Paul felt a tap on his shoulder and heard Bill say, "For Christ's sake! Couldn't you wait until you were inside the car to make love to her?" If looks could kill, Bill would've been dead. With his familiar voice of authority Paul yelled, "Get down here and help me! Can't you see that she's hurt?" Bill walked past the situation to the Oriental woman and asked, "What is going on?" Dee started to speak rapidly in broken English. Within a few minutes, she'd explained the whole situation to Bill. With his newfound knowledge, Bill practically ran to his cousin saying, "Come on, let's get out of here!" Paul replied, "We can't go without Kitty." Bill told Paul that there was no need to wait for Kitty because she was dead.

In an instant, the men had lifted my body off of the ground. Bill was at my feet and Paul carried the upper half of my body to the large, dark car that had rolled out of the jungle's edge. The man that had been sitting in the passengers seat stepped out of the car with a machine gun in his hand while I was being helped into the back seat of the vehicle. Paul and Dee seated themselves each at one of my sides. As we began to speed away, shots were fired in our direction. Japanese soldiers held their ground, sending a multitude of bullets at our vehicle while the other Korean and Japanese soldiers filed into a jeep.

Bill was driving at the speed of lightening. As we roared past another jungle road that lead off to the right, Bill flashed the headlights off and then on again. Seconds later, an open jeep filled with undercover agents sped past us. They were headed for the Bungalow. Paul looked back in the direction they had come from. He could hear the undercover agents' machine guns being fired. Paul wished the best of luck. They would need it, and then some.

As we drove, I was in a vast amount of pain. Tears were rolling down my cheeks but I did not say a word to anyone. I was just grateful to be alive. Poor Kitty, I thought. I had said so many wrong things about her. I could only hope that God would forgive me. Kitty had died for our country. She had put herself in the face of danger to protect Dee and me and gone to her death for her efforts. I owed this woman so much and now it was too late to make amends with her. One thing was for sure; I would make a map to show the President the exact location of the hidden bombs.

Paul was worried about the consequences the night had foretold. Every single one of them was now in danger. It was going to be tough to get the women out of the country.

I could no longer bear the pain. As we drove along the highway, my body slumped over. I'd passed out in my seat. Dee, who was watching out for her mistress, reached over and pushed my body back against the seat. Paul, who'd been off in another world was surprised when he turned his head and saw my body. He felt my pulse. It was weak and I was still passed out.

As Bill turned the car into the driveway of Paul's estate the morning sunrise broke the darkness, bringing on a new day. Bill stepped out of the car saying, "I don't mind telling you all that was a drive from Hell." He and the man holding a machine gun walked around the car, inspecting for any kind of danger. When they were through with the inspection, Bill waved his hand at Paul. All was well and it was safe to get out of the car.

Paul carried Joyce in his arms to the house. Dee was at his heels. Bill stood on the front porch, guarding the house. The man with the machine gun went to walk around the estate. Paul carried Joyce inside of the house, through the corridor and to the back of the house. He'd chosen the bedroom that was next to his for Joyce to reside in.

Paul laid Joyce on the bed and immediately began cutting her gown off. It had bloodstains on it and he wanted to see if she had an open wound. He stripped her down to pantaloon bottoms and a thin, cotton chemise top. Dee silently stood in the background, guarding her 'Missy' from any more danger until Paul turned around and asked her to go and find the maid. He needed the maid to bring bandages, soap and water. Dee and the maid returned a few minutes later with the items.

Forty-five minutes later, Paul completed his examination of Joyce. She had several bad bruises and two cracked ribs. There were no broken bones. She had been lucky.

I awoke late in the afternoon. I'd slept for a long time. I opened my eyes and glanced around the room. Dee was sitting in the stuffed chair next to the bed. As soon as I saw her she said, "Oh Missy, you awake now. I go now and get you something to eat." During Dee's absence I observed the room. Light shades of blue and green were predominating in the room and it was gorgeous. French doors opened onto a screen-covered porch. The porch led to an open terrace that ran the entire length of the house.

When Dee returned she found me sitting outside at the white wicker table on the porch. The chair I was sitting in had a tall woven back that reached high above my head. On the other side of the table there was a matching chair. She set a tray of food on the table and seated herself in the other chair. I ate every last bite of food on the tray. It was American cooking and a wonderful treat.

The view from the porch was beautiful. Flowers were everywhere. In the center of the terrace there was fountain that sprayed water out in every direction. Several small, colored birds swept down onto the terrace to enjoy morning baths. It was lovely to sit outside. I could hear Dee inside of the room. She was straightening it up. When I entered the room, I saw a pale yellow, long gown lying on the bed. Thank God that I no longer had to dress in only white clothing. I was glad to see that some of my clothes from Virginia were packed and brought here. Dee had prepared a bath for me, which I knew I would enjoy.

Dee loved to fix my hair. Since it was difficult for me to lift my right arm I appreciated her help. I was glad she was with me. As she dressed me, I noticed that she was excited. I asked her what all of the excitement was about and she replied, "It's a surprise Missy!" When she was through dressing me she led me out into a wide hallway. Double doors that connected the hall and the terrace below were wide open. When we were outside, Dee insisted I sit on a gray, stone colored bench. Relieved to see that it had a back caused me not to argue with her. As I was seated, Dee clapped her hands together and said, "Look towards the edge of the forest!" I turned myself around on the bench and saw Laverne standing over there.

"Oh, I can't believe it. You're here!" I exclaimed. She and I began running towards each other; each of us had tears of joy rolling down our faces. We met in the middle of the garden, throwing our arms around one another. Both of us were speaking as we held each other closely.

After breaking free from each other, Laverne stood back and scanned me from head to toe. When she was through, she said, "You've lost a great deal of weight. You look ill. Bill and Paul told me what happened to you. You must be careful! I don't know what I'd do if I lost you." "Oh," I replied, "you'd manage. There's always Bill." Laverne grinned, "Yea! I guess so but we're only friends, mind you." "Sure," I said, "sure!"

We found a bench in the shade of the forest to sit on. I was grateful to be off of my feet. Laverne was simply glad to be with her companion again. We talked all afternoon about what had happened to each of us since the day we'd eaten lunch at the Inn in Virginia.

Dee spent her entire afternoon on the screen porch of her Missy's room. She could see the women sitting on the bench enjoying the jungle's shade. This was not a safe place for her Missy to be. Someone could easily circle around her back and take her away from here. As she sat there and watching the two friends chat, she started feeling sorry for herself. She thought that because Missy had her companion back she would not be needed for much longer. She loved Missy and where would someone as young as she go in such a hostile world like this? She would have to hide because they'd be looking for her. She was tired of hiding. Out loud she said, "I pray to God that Missy not send me away."

As Laverne and I visited, I noticed that Bill was circling the outer bounds of the terrace. Each time he did he made a point of letting Laverne know that he was there. He would stand in one place until Laverne looked up and noticed his presence. After she did, he would wave to her and then walk around again. Each time he circled the grounds; he got closer and closer to the bench we were sitting on. One of my ribs was beginning to ache. I told Laverne that I needed to go back to my room and rest. Instead of following me, she stood by the bench and waited for Bill.

Only once, did I glance back at them. They had left the terrace and hand in hand, were heading for the shade of a tree. As I neared the stairs that led back to my room, I saw that Dee was waiting to help me up them. I was glad to see her and said, "Hi! What have you been doing today?" She replied, "I wait for Missy to come back. I not like your back to the shadows of the trees." I was surprised at myself. After all that had recently happened to me, I had been so careless. I decided that it was not going to happen again. "Why, thank you, Dee. Thank you for watching out for me. I don't know what I would do without you."

Inside my room, Dee helped me undress. She slipped a long, white cotton gown over my head. I didn't mind wearing white because it was the coolest color to wear in the heat. The bed and it's cool white sheets felt wonderful. The overhead fan was whispering softly as it spun cool air down on my face. I was much more tired than I had realized and fell right to sleep.

I awoke in pitch darkness. Something woke me up. I looked around and saw that the adjoining door was open. Paul was standing inside of the doorway. He quietly walked over to the chair next to my bed and sat down. I think that he thought that I was still sleeping because he didn't say a word. After a few moments, he stretched his legs out and leaned his head on the back of the chair. We both fell to sleep.

I awoke again just before dawn. Outside, the wind and rain were pounding against the walls of the house. We were in the rainy season and it would rain everyday until winter. I looked over and saw that the chair next to my bed was empty. Paul was gone.

I was slept out. No longer tired, I reached to the foot of my bed for my long-sleeved, white robe. I got out of bed, slipped the robe on and tied the sash around my waist. I went outside on the screen porch. I saw a small form huddled up against my bedroom wall. Dee had taken the porch chair's pillows and made a bed out of them. I reached down to wake her up. Her skin was cool to the touch. Fear ran through my body like the blade of a knife. I could stand no more. I began screaming. I screamed and screamed.

Hearing the first scream, Paul shot out of his bed. He ran through the doors that adjoined his room to Joyce's. He found Joyce on the porch holding a small form in her arms. She was rocking it back and forth, sobbing uncontrollably. Owen, who was on guard, had run up the stairs and stood viewing the same scene as Paul. Bill had run along the pathway to Paul's house and stopped dead in his tracks when he saw Joyce. He ran his hands through his red hair and said, "God, how could you have let this happen? Weren't you on guard Owen?" Owen replied, still in awe, "Yes sir, I was."

Paul pulled me away from Dee. "No, I can't leave her," I cried. Paul softly whispered, "Please come back to your room with me. There's not enough room for Bill to examine her with us there. She might still be alive." I went back into my room and sat on the side of the bed, waiting for Paul's return.

Nearly an hour and a half later, he came back into my room. I looked up at him with fear in my eyes. I dreaded what might come out of his mouth.

Paul sat down beside me and reached for my hand. He placed it inside of his and I knew that this was a bad sign. I braced myself for the worst and was able to tell him that I was all right. "Go ahead, tell me." I said. "Dee's going to be fine. We got to her in time. We were able to close the wound and stop the bleeding." I sighed in relief and asked him what had happened. Paul explained, "Sometime after it quit raining, she must've seen something out in the jungle. Owen found blood on the bench that is near the edge of the forest. Someone stabbed her twice. Once in the side and once in her right shoulder. She lost a lot of blood and is going to have to be watched closely." "Oh, thank God." I said, "I'll watch her recovery myself."

Paul replied, "I think not. First of all, you yourself are not well and secondly, I need you to help me. But before anything else happens, I want you to dress yourself and tell me exactly what happened back at the Bungalow. I need to know everything that happened the night that Kitty was killed. I'll send Laverne up to help you get dressed and then I need you to come down to the sitting room. Word for word, we all need to know exactly what happened." Paul rose from the side of the bed. He said, "Right now I've got to make a call regarding the security of this house. One man guarding this house is not enough."

Laverne entered my room quite some time later. She looked very drawn and rung out. Maybe, I thought it was just the light brown dress that she was wearing. As I observed at a closer angle, I saw that she had huge black circles under her eyes. She also looked ill. While I was dressed, neither of us spoke a word. We were both lost in our own private thoughts. Each of us knew that it was going to take a miracle to get back to the states alive.

When Laverne and I entered the sitting room, I was surprised by the amount of people that were already seated. I wondered where they had come from. I saw that Paul had placed a chair for me next to his. The chairs faced the audience. There was a table with a pitcher of ice water and glasses next to my chair.

After everyone had been seated a gray haired man by the name of Bob Hillroy stood up from his chair in the back of the room. I could tell by all of the medals he wore that he was a high-ranked official in the air force. Paul seemed to know him quite well. "Paul," he said, "I believe it would be to our best advantage if the other woman spoke first." Laverne looked at me in surprise. I knew that she hated to speak in public. I felt sorry for my friend.

Bill was sitting in the back row of chairs with all of the other officers. He stood up, dressed in full uniform and said, "Sir, if I may have a word with Laverne I believe she'll be able to speak." He too was a high-ranking officer but wore fewer medals than Mr. Bob Hillroy. He walked over to Laverne and kneeled at her side. For several minutes, he whispered in her ear. He rose from the floor and squeezed her hand, pulling her out of the chair to face the people.

I was silent as I listened to her speak. I realized that she had also been through a lot. I wondered if God would ever forgive me for inflicting such pain on her dear soul. The Officers questioned Laverne first and then it was my turn. I could see why Paul had set up the table beside me. I drank half of the pitcher of ice water while Laverne was questioned. The questions went on and on. After three hours, they finally came to an end.

The dark walnut table in the dining room had been expanded to accommodate the guests. The narrow, white linen tablecloth was draped over the table and had a floral arrangement placed in it's center. Various cold cuts, cheeses and fruits were accessible to all of the guests. The men picked up their plates from the sideboard and begin filling them with food, conversing with each other the entire time. I had seen and heard all that I wanted to so I left the others and headed down the corridor to my room.

I was surprised to see Paul sitting in the chair next to my bed when I entered the room. I asked, "Why aren't you eating with your fellow officers?" He said, "Because, I'd rather eat with you." Paul had a table set up next to the rose garden for us to dine at. The roses were still blooming and their scent was almost intoxicating.

I felt a bit uncomfortable sitting so close to the notorious bench at the edge of the jungle; the one Dee had been stabbed at. So much had happened since yesterday. "Paul, how is Dee?" I asked. "Well," he said, "she'll carry a pretty nasty scar on her shoulder. I think her assassin was aiming for her heart. In time, she'll be as good as new. If you're uneasy sitting this close to where Dee was stabbed, I'll have the table moved closer to the house."

He raised his hand high above his head, signaling something. A split second later, men stepped out from the thick of the jungle with machineguns in hand. They made a complete circle around us. I laughed and said, "Well Paul, I see we're safe but now we've lost our privacy." "How is it that I always lose when you're around?" he questioned. My voice, serious replied, "Paul you haven't lost. You've just won my undying gratitude."

For the next three days, Paul and I worked from dawn until dusk on the map. The situation around the estate was critical. There was a pinched look about Paul's face. I knew that he had a lot going on that I was not aware of. But, I had no idea about how bad the whole situation really was.

Laverne had been moved to a small cottage just a few feet in distance from the terrace area of Paul's house. I hardly had time to say anything to my friend. I was holed up with Paul in his office. Our food was even brought to the office by a small Korean man. He looked to be in his early twenties and seemed to know of everything going on at the estate. Paul seemed to trust this man whose name was Ron. Whenever I left the room, I could hear the two of them speaking in low tones.

It had been ten days since Paul and I had begun working on the map. My ribs were nicely mending themselves. I was simply exhausted. I needed some time to myself, to replenish my energy and to be in touch with my soul. The next morning I approached Paul with my suggestion. He agreed and allowed me to take the afternoon off. I was simply delighted.

Since Dee's accident, I'd been taking care of myself, including my hair. I didn't mind having to do this; after all, I'd been taking care of myself all of my life. Although the pain I felt when I lifted my arms had considerably diminished it was not completely gone.

All that I could think about as I worked with Paul was being able to take a long, hot bath. I would be able to wash my hair and dress myself in something feminine and exceptionally pretty. I'd already picked the gown that I would wear. I was so excited to have the afternoon to myself.

I had no more than leaned back in the bathtub when Laverne came walking in. She looked nice in her pale green gown. We chatted the entire time that I soaked in the warm water. When the time came to wash my hair came, Laverne washed it for me. During the time that it took for my hair to dry, we discussed everything. The only exception in our conversation was the one thing that was bothering both of us the most; how afraid we were of what the new day might bring.

That evening wound up being a night to remember. It was a night of celebration and lately, no one in this household had experienced anything to celebrate. That evening, we all gathered around the large table in the dining room. Laverne looked beautiful in her dark blue gown and for once, Bill's red hair was groomed, every hair was in place. He looked handsome in the dark blue/gray suit he was wearing. I smiled as he walked over and stood next to Laverne. The two had become inseparable.

Paul stood at the head of the table but had made no move indicating that it was time to be seated. I was standing at the opposite end of the table because I didn't want him to think that I had to sit near him. Paul studied me from his end. I hoped that I looked good enough to impress his eyes. I was wearing a low-necked, emerald green gown that was cut off at the shoulders.

I was beginning to think we would stand behind our chairs all night when another couple entered the room. Dee had just arrived and was being lead to the table by the young Oriental man that worked so closely with Paul, Ron. I was so glad to see her that I left the table so I could give her a hug. As I held her little frame next to mine, she whispered, "I so glad to see you!" "And, I you!" I said.

Paul waved his hand in the air, signaling to everyone that it was time to be seated. Not sure exactly where my place was, I walked to the chair I had stood behind earlier. Paul looked down the length of the table and said, "Everyone sit down except you." I was standing at the foot of the table, glancing around trying to figure out whom Paul had addressed as the exception. I saw that his eyes were on me and he had just pointed his finger in my direction. I asked, "Paul, are you talking to me?" He answered, "Yes, I am! You don't belong there." Because I didn't know where I did belong, I immediately became defensive. I shouted, "Don't you dare try to tell me where I belong! And, don't ever point your finger at me again. I simply will not tolerate such rudeness!" "Come here," Paul said. "No I won't." I replied.

Laverne and Bill were grinning at each other. Dee and Ron were also exchanging amused looks. Paul, with his usual voice of authority repeated himself, "I said you're standing in the wrong place, come here!" My lip quivered, as I said, "No, I won't!" Paul bellowed out, "For Heaven's sake, what is wrong with you now?" "I'll tell you what is wrong with me; you're an overbearing ox! I don't know where I belong." I said, quite angrily. I raced out of the room with tears streaming down my cheeks. I was headed for the sanctity of my room.

Paul left the table to race after me. As he ran, I heard him say, "Oh, no you don't young lady." I raced through the door of my room, swinging it shut in his face. The door swung open, hitting the wall because it had hit Paul's shoulder with such force. He stood inside of my room, straightening the jacket of his dark gray suit. He was still breathing hard when he said, "Well now, what seems to be bothering you?" "Oh, I'll tell you what's bothering me," I said. But before I could finish, he cut me off by telling me to be careful and not say anything I would regret, spoiling the party. I responded, "I spoiled the party? Don't you dare put the blame on me." Paul's voice softly said, "Come here." I asked him why and his response was touching. He said, "Because I want to tell you where you belong."

As we left the room Bill told everyone to sit down. He squeezed Laverne's shoulder and then he left the room. He re-entered a few minutes later. All eyes were on him and in unison, everyone asked, "Well, what's happening?" Bill stood looking at them. He put both of his hands into his pockets, rocked back and forth on his heels as he replied, "Well, nothing that shouldn't have happened a long time ago." Laverne began to laugh. She laughed and laughed at the irony of the whole situation. She was laughing so hard that she almost fell off of her chair. The others had joined her and they all laughed together until Bill said, "Okay, everyone. Let's eat. I'm starving." "Not without your guest of honor." Paul's voice rang from the doorway. He guided me to the chair that was next to his.

Laverne sat directly across from me and Bill was seated next to her. Throughout dinner, Laverne tried to catch my attention. She would hold up her left hand for a few seconds and then put it down again. Finally, I caught on and saw that she was wearing a huge solitaire diamond. This was her way of telling me that she was engaged.

We were all having such a good time around the table that no one bothered to check the time. We talked and laughed until eleven o'clock. Paul took his fork and gently tapped it against his crystal wine glass, which was filled half way with white wine. Our talking ceased. We all waited in anticipation of what he was about to say.

"First off," he said, "all of our hard team work has paid off. The map which shows the location of the hidden bombs and the surrounding areas was finished as of three o'clock this afternoon." All of us began to clap our hands together. We raised our wine glasses in the air and then drank to the occasion. Paul raised his hand to silence us and continued, "We owe a great deal to these ladies sitting beside us. I ask that Laverne and Joyce stand."

We stood up at the same time. Paul walked over to Laverne and said, "I give this to you Laverne as a token of my appreciation." He pulled out a small black jewelry box and opened it. He took a long gold necklace out of the box and fastened it around Laverne's neck. She blushed from the attention Paul was giving her. She sat down, fingering the chain.

I raced around the table to get a better look at the necklace. The gold chain held a gold angel with small wings and in the center of the angel was a large diamond. It was exquisite. Paul looked at me and said, "Back to your seat young lady. Your turn is coming." As I circled the table, he didn't take his eyes off of me. As I returned to my seat (a bit nervous) I said, "Well everyone, one thing is for sure. That is that I won't be given an angel necklace." Everyone, including myself burst out laughing.

Paul asked me to close my eyes. "You're peeking. I can tell because your eye lashes are fluttering," he said. "Now, hold out your left hand." I did as I was told. I felt a ring slip onto the fourth finger of my left hand. I opened my eyes to see the largest, greenest emerald that I'd ever seen on my hand. I gasped and whispered, "Oh Paul, it's simply gorgeous! I don't know what to say. Paul looked into my eyes and said that he only needed to hear one word. "Yes, yes, yes!" I replied.

We held each other for a long time in front of my bedroom door. He teased me, saying, "I don't know if giving you the ring was a good idea or not. Now, I don't feel comfortable sitting in your room while you sleep." He turned on his heel and left me standing there, alone.

Isn't it strange, I thought? You wait all of your life for that one special man to enter your life so you can share the rest of it together and now that my man was here, I was afraid.

It had been the most wonderful night of my life. Everyone had needed to laugh and be merry and I don't know if I had ever had such a wonderful time laughing and just being happy. Laverne had offered to help me undress but I would hear nothing of it. The time we had left to spend with each other was becoming shorter every second and I knew that she needed to be alone with Bill. Besides, I needed to be alone so I could drift away in thought.

Now, that the map was completed and I would be going home. As of today, I had accomplished the job that I was brought here to do. I thought of Kitty. Without the part she had played in my mission, I would have failed.

Instead of changing into my nightgown, I chose to put on a long tailored, slate blue gown. The sleeves were long and cuffed and it had a high collar, which was piped in black satin. The dress was heavier than what I usually wore. However, I felt chilled. I had just opened the French door. I turned the stuffed chair by my bed to face the door. I sat down. I wanted to see past the screen-covered porch and see the sunrise. I had not been in touch with my God lately. I began to pray.

Just as everyone was milling around the house preparing for the new day, the first shots rang out. Within seconds, you could hear everyone's feet scurrying along the wood floors. From where I stood I could see the guards running toward the edge of the jungle. Soon, a jeep appeared. It stopped only long enough to pick up the men with the machine guns that had just fired at the house. Once the men were loaded into the jeep it roared off speeding down the wide pathway that went straight into the heart of the jungle.

Paul sailed through the adjoining door of our rooms, flying towards me. "Oh, there you are! Thank God, you're dressed. Start packing all of your things. We've got to get you out of here. All Hell's breaking loose! You have half an hour to get ready. Bill's gone to tell Laverne."

I watched as he headed past Laverne's small cottage. He went down the widened pathway that wound itself through the row of bamboo huts that the guards were staying in. At one time, this land had been a small Korean village. Moments later, the five guards that had been left to guard the estate were moving large arm fulls of brush. They were uncovering a runway.

Fifteen minutes later, Laverne and I had packed and were ready to leave. We went downstairs and I saw Dee standing in one of the corners of the sitting room. She had not packed anything. I questioned her about not being packed. She replied, "I not know if you would want me." A bit shocked, I said, "Of course I want you. Hurry! Run and get all of your things!" Dee ran out of the room. Only a few minutes passed before she returned. Her clothes were tied together with a piece of cloth.

Bill hit the door, running. He said, "I'll take Laverne and Dee to one of the helicopters. Paul will be here shortly for you." I watched as Bill, Laverne and Dee ran down the runway. The helicopters were in motion, ready to take us away to safety. A shot rang out and barely missed Bill as he was shoving Laverne into the helicopter. The man who had been standing beside Bill was hit. He fell down on the airstrip either wounded or dead. I stood on the screened porch waiting for Paul. I was horrified.

More shots rang out. Two of the guards were hit and their bodies slumped onto the ground. Bill yelled to Paul, "Sniper in the trees! I'm going after him." Paul saw another guerrilla soldier coming out of the jungle. The soldier had his pistol pointed at Paul. Paul, gun in hand, fired. His bullet hit home. Paul ran to the steps I was waiting on and grabbed my arm with one hand and my suitcase with the other. We started running to the remaining helicopter.

Another shot rang out and hit the guard that had been guarding Paul and me as we ran. Another shot rang out. This time, Paul dropped my suitcase to the ground and grabbed his gun. It was too late to fire. Three Japanese guerrillas surrounded us. We were only a few feet away from the helicopter. We had almost made it.

It seemed that the Japanese guerrillas were waiting for someone. I wondered who it was. It wasn't long before I received my answer. Lee Yeng was walking towards us. He was walking as if he had all of the time in the world. He looked just as handsome as ever and my heart fluttered. I was still attracted to this man. If it hadn't been for Paul, in another lifetime . . .

Lee walked to us and stopped only about three feet away from Paul and me. He was standing directly in front of me. Another Japanese soldier stood in front of Paul. Lee was studying me up and down. I looked over at the Japanese soldier. I'd seen him in my dreams; the ones I'd written the President about. In my dream, he stood three feet in front of me with the same large, black eyes. Those eyes had been filled with hate just as they were now. In the dream, he reached into the pocket of his uniform just as he was doing now. And as the dream had foretold, the soldier brought out a gun and was aiming it at my heart.

I stood, transfixed. I was unable to move. I'd just watched my dream become reality. I knew I was going to die. The whole time that we'd been standing here facing the enemy, Paul had been inching toward me. The cruel-looking Japanese soldier asked Paul for the map. Paul looked him straight in the eyes and said, "I'm afraid you're a little late, my friend. The map is halfway to America."

Lee Yeng had moved forward and was standing only a foot away from me. He said, "Come with me. I will protect you." I replied, "No. I can not" And then, the Japanese soldier said, "Kill her, you fool!" He turned his gun away from Paul, aimed it at me and fired. Paul pushed me aside and took the bullet in his shoulder. The Japanese soldier aimed and fired at me again.

Lee Yeng raised his gun, fired and shot Paul. He slid down to the ground. Again, the Japanese soldier aimed and fired his gun at me. Upon seeing this, Lee stepped between the bullet and me. He took the bullet in the chest. His body slumped to the ground, at my feet. Before the Japanese soldier could fire his gun, a bullet came from behind me, whizzed past my head and hit him in the head. He was dead before he even hit the ground.

I looked behind me and saw Bill and Owen running toward me. Bill yelled, "Get her out of here!" Owen picked me up and ran with me to the helicopter. "No, No! I can't leave him lying there! Let me down so I can go to him!" I screamed.

Owen threw the body of the pilot out of the door. He pushed me into the vacant seat. Owen was at the controls and within seconds, we were air borne. I was flying to the plane that was waiting to take me home. I looked down from the helicopter at the spot where Paul's body was laid. Bill was beside him, on his knees with his hand placed against Paul's heart.

Tears were there, inside of me. I was sobbing but the tears would not come out. It was strange how fate can make a complete circle in one's life. I thought that Owen had meant to harm me in New York. Instead, he had saved my life, casting Paul's away.

When I boarded the plane with Dee and Laverne, I was oblivious to everything including them. I had locked myself inside of a place that only I could go, deep inside of me. No one could find me here and here, I could die alone in grief and solitude. Now, that Paul was gone I no longer wished to live.

Several times Laverne and Dee came and sat beside me, trying to comfort me. I had the window seat and I was lost somewhere out in the clouds. I wasn't even aware that either of them had sat beside me.

Owen had boarded the plane to protect the women. Paul had made him promise that if anything happened to him, he'd see them to safety. I wasn't in the least bit surprised when we landed at the airport in Virginia. Owen helped me from my seat and held my arm as we walked down the runway. The same chauffeur was waiting for just as he had been that day in June.

It seemed that a thousand years had passed since we'd first arrived in Virginia. In actuality, it was only the fifth day of October. October was the month my moon was set in. It was the month that controlled and governed my heart. I wondered, what heart? My heart was as dead as Paul was.

When we arrived at the house, John and Martha were standing in front of the house to greet us. First, Martha hugged me and then John. Martha led us inside of the house to the sitting room. Tea was waiting to be served. John, her husband had stayed outside to speak with Owen. They stood outside talking for a very long time.

As we drank the tea, Martha and Laverne talked non-stop. I was sitting in the chair that was closest to the main entry hall. Dee stood behind me with a sad expression on her face. She did not like it when her mistress grieved. Dee thought she'd soon be dead if she didn't stop.

Eventually, we were shown to the same rooms we'd stayed in before. Dee was given the bedroom adjoining mine.

Often times she had to come and wake me from the bad dreams I'd been experiencing since Paul's death.

Each day was like the other. In one sense of the word, I was glad to be staying in Paul's house. It made me feel closer to him. On the other hand, I seemed to see him everywhere. Laverne and Martha had become the best of friends. They constantly had endless conversations.

Several weeks had passed and we were having one of the warmer days before the season gave way to winter. I felt like walking. I walked and walked, finding trails that I had not known existed. Growing tired, I began making my way back to the plantation. I knew that Owen wasn't far away from me. He seemed to have appointed himself as my personal bodyguard and we went everywhere together.

I stepped on the pathway leading from the woods and onto the edge of the lawn. It was then, that I saw a car parked in front of the house. Bill was just getting out of the driver's seat. He opened the car's rear door and was helping a man out of the car. Once the man was out of the car, Bill handed him a cane to walk with. My heart stood still. I asked Owen if he saw what I saw. He said he did.

I looked closer at the man in the distance. He was wearing a dark brown suit, leaning against the cane. I exclaimed, "It's Paul, Owen! It's Paul!" I began to run. Owen passed in front of me with his large frame shaking the ground every time his foot went down. Owen, a distance ahead of me reached Paul and I could see him patting Paul on the back and shaking his hand.

Paul asked, "How is she? She looks frail. Have you been taking good care of her?" Owen replied, "I've tried hard, Boss. I'm glad you came back when you did. Now that you're home, she'll be just fine." Owen walked over to Bill. He greeted him, saying, "Lordy, Lordy! Man, I'm glad to see you. Let's go on inside Bill and let those two love birds get reacquainted."

I slowed to a walk for the last few feet between Paul and I. My eyes touched and locked with his. Never had I felt such love and such pain at the same time. It was as if our souls had touched and were intervening, uniting as one. Building an everlasting flame.

Paul dropped his cane to the ground and opened his arms. I walked into his arms and he held me tightly. At last, he was home with me. Love that would be with us now and forever!

To Write Or Not Write The President

During the course of years we spent working together in the small diet office of the hospital, Ginny Farvelle, Tina O'Banion and I became very good friends. They reminded me, ever so often, that I needed to write a letter to the President to inform him of the bombs hidden in North Korea. For a reason unbeknownst to me, I kept putting the letter off. My friends reminded me month after month to write the letter but I was still hesitant and still didn't know why I felt this way.

Several weeks after I'd received one of the friendly reminders, I knew the time had come for me to make a final decision on writing the letter. With the scrutiny of war and actual wars being fought in other countries printed, almost daily, in the paper I knew the letter needed to be written now or never. I decided to ask my Heavenly Father for His guidance and help with this. I then knew that if I was meant to write the letter I would have a dream about it. A few nights passed before I did have the dream that gave me the answer I'd been searching for.

I dreamed that my letter, in it's long white envelope was received by the President. After he read the contents of the letter, the President turned the matter over to an official who was considered as high up in the government and a man who held the President's trust.

Several weeks after I had sent the letter I received a reply from the President's secretary. The letter stated that the President wished to speak to me about the matter in person. He wanted me to fly to Washington D.C. so we could meet at the White House. Days later, I found myself checking into a large hotel, near the White House, to wait for a summons from the President. After I'd settled down in my room I received a message from the President's secretary. I read that my appointment was scheduled the next morning at ten o'clock.

That night I did not sleep well. I continually mulled each and everything over in my mind. I rose the next morning a little past seven o'clock. I ate an early breakfast in the hotel dining room and then went back to my room to dress for the appointment. I settled on wearing a cool crème pants suit and matching heels.

It was late in the summer and the weather was hot and humid. I was grateful that my appointment was in the morning instead of in the hot afternoon. I hoped that it would rain and cool things down again.

I picked up my matching crème handbag, slipped the tapes I'd recorded information about the bombs onto, inside of the handbag and snapped it shut. I headed out of my room, to the elevator and landed in the hotel lobby. I informed the desk clerk that I would be leaving at fifteen minutes after six the following morning and then exited through the main doors of the hotel. I asked the doorman to wave down a cab for me. I waited only a few seconds before a yellow cab pulled up to the curb. Minutes later, the cab pulled up in front of the White House. I paid the fair, gave the driver a tip and than began up the stairs that led to the front entrance of the White House.

A tall, beefy-faced man met me upon my arrival inside the corridor. I observed that life had surely been good to him for he was more than a bit on the stout side. I did not like the man's dark eyes. They held a beady look. The eyes are the windows of the soul and what I saw in this man gave me an uneasy feeling. There was something I did not like about this man. I pictured what my daughter, Susan would say if she were with me, "Look for trouble Mother and you'll certainly find it."

I knew I should not have come from the very moment I shook hands with the President and looked into his cautious gray/blue with a tinge of yellow flecks, eyes. The President was going to be a non-believer. In the beginning, he seemed to be friendly enough. However, from the tone of his voice I knew he thought of me as a fake and was not going to take anything I said seriously. The President soon brought the short interview to a close. I thanked him as I stood up and then headed for the door. A man stood at each side of the door. One of the men was the heavy set man I had met earlier and the other man was of a medium build and jet-black hair. As I exited the room I noticed that neither of the men looked directly at me. They followed me into the hall and than began to lead me in the opposite direction I had entered the room. I felt that we were near the side or the back of the house. They guided me to a set of stairs that led down into an alley, which could be seen, from the fenced yard.

I descended the stairs, one at a time, thinking about how foolish it was for me to have come to Washington, D.C. let alone taking time to do this. The trip had been a dismal failure from the start. Just as I had stepped onto the green grass of the lawn I heard the beefy-faced man yell, "Hey you, down there, you were a fool to think the President would ever believe the likes of you! You are a fake and not at all what you profess yourself to be." I became furious. I'd taken my last cent so I could make this trip and now I was being ridiculed just as I'd always been when I was a child. The beefy-faced man continued, "Hell, woman! We're trying to start a war not stop it."

His reply had made me so angry I sped up five stairs without even realizing I'd done so. I yelled up at him, "You fool, don't you have enough sense to realize that the war will lead to the holy war and the end of the world?" The man in the brown suit with dark hair and eyes spoke up. "War is good for the politicians. Go home, no one is going to believe you!" "Oh, yeah?" I yelled. "Well how do you think your high up official is going to like having his story published on the front page of your newspaper? His secret is out! He has a nine-year-old illegitimate son with a beautiful call girl. She had long legs, curly dark hair, and dark brown eyes but she couldn't fight against the odds any longer. She was wearing red when she recently slashed her wrist. She gave up and now; she is dead and buried because of her self-inflicted wounds. Well, I can tell both of you cricked bastards that I'm going to do something about this and you can read about it in the morning paper! Let's see how your high and mighty official feels about me then!"

As the beefy-faced man took the stairs two at a time he yelled to the darker man, telling him to call the father of the nine year old child and let him know he had trouble because she knew. Seeing the stout man coming at me in his medium shade blue/gray suit, I broke into a run. Within seconds, the man knocked me against the steel wire fence that enclosed the grounds of the White House. I fell to the ground. The beefy-faced man stood over with me with his legs spread and his arms crossed. He was glaring down at me when he said, "You damn witch! You just couldn't leave well enough alone, could you? Now you can pay the piper and here he comes!" I stared into the cold blue and gray eyes of the man.

Neither of the men bothered to assist me up to a standing position. I grasped the wire fence and pulled myself up. As I dusted my cream pants off I noticed grass stains covering one side of my pant leg and both of my knees. I had used my knees to brace my fall. I stood tall as I turned and squarely faced the man with the gray hair. I held my head high, bracing myself for what I knew was coming.

Moments later, the man with the brown suit pulled up in an expensive gray town car. The man with the gray hair turned to both men and said, "You two did a good job screwing things up. If either of you had used your heads in this matter . . . Now I have to finish what the two of you should have already done." He walked over and stood beside the town car. The dark man opened the door on the driver's side and waited for the official to make his way under the steering wheel. After the official was inside the car the dark man shut the door. The beefy-faced man grabbed my arm, walked me around the car to the passenger's side, opened the door and threw me inside. He fastened the seatbelt firmly around my body and slammed the door. Then he took an instrument out of his pocket and sealed the door on my side shut. I reached over to try to unlock the door but it would not budge.

As the instrument had sealed the door it all became crystal clear to me; I was going to die in this car. I just didn't know exactly when or where my death would be taking place. The car began to move forward. The two men had already opened the gates so that we could leave the grounds of the White House. In a short amount of time we headed out of the city, traveling down a freeway leading to God knows where. The man with the gray hair who was driving the car began speaking to me. "Ms. Torri, I'm really sorry that your trip to Washington, D.C. has turned out so bad for you. I also apologize that you've been caught up in this political situation. You're dangerous to us and I do not like what I have to do. I wish it could have been different for both of us. You really are quite a woman and for the record, I'm convinced you are psychic, very psychic indeed."

I simply folded my arms and did not say a word as the car traveled on and on. I knew the man found my silence greatly perturbing. He'd probably thought I was going to confess all of my troubles to him. Well, he had another thought coming as I had nothing to say to him.

As the sunset neared, it seemed we had reached our destination. The ocean could be seen for as far as the human eye could see. It was a beautiful shade of blue. I knew those blue waters would be opening their arms to greet me any moment. This was to be my grave and no one would know. The man had driven the car along the ocean until he found a remote area off of the main highway. The car was parked along the edge of the cliff.

I had to act quickly because if I was to die than so was he; I'd take this man down with me. With the power of my mind I sealed every door shut. It didn't matter how hard someone tried to open the door because unless I released them, the doors would remain shut. I knew that the man's intention was to shove me off, in the car, of the cliff. The beefy-faced man, who had started all of this, would soon be arriving alone to pick the official up. What they didn't know was that my powers could move objects, make tires flat, and much more.

The man with the gray hair took the car out of gear and started to open his door. He tried several times to get the door open but his efforts were to no avail. Beads of sweat had formed on his forehead. He leaned back against the seat, reached into his pocket and pulled a white linen handkerchief out. He mopped the sweat from his brow and tried to open the door again. The door remained shut. The man began to push on the door with all of his body's weight, which caused the car to rock back and forth. I sat silently as I watched him struggle. He snapped at me, "You damn witch! Let me out of here!" Very calmly I replied, "Not on your life. If I go down then so do you."

He tried to open the automatic windows but they also remained closed. As far as the man with the gray hair was concerned, this was the last straw. He completely lost control of himself. He pounded on the glass with his fist but it did not break. He began mumbling, crying and screaming at me, all at the same time.

A few seconds earlier, I noticed that because the car was out of gear we'd begun rolling forward. The car was inching toward the edge of the cliff and soon we would be plummeting down the embankment and into the ocean water. He also seemed to sense this because he had stopped his ridiculous fit. His face was ash white and he did not speak even one word. He shoved his foot on the brake but found that the brakes were not working. The car continued rolling, inch by inch, toward the edge.

Suddenly, I came to my senses. I realized that all of the tests I had done in my earlier years, to see how strong and powerful I could be, could be used now. I could do something about this. I did not want to die and I did not want the man sitting beside me to die either. I had almost allowed my temper and thoughts of revenge destroy both of us. I did not have the right to take this man's life, only God has that right. I glanced over at him. His body was hunched over the steering wheel. He was holding his face in his hands, sobbing. He did not want to die.

The car had rolled to the very edge of the cliff before I realized. Suddenly we went over the edge. The car had dropped to only twenty feet above the ocean when I was able to finally take some control of the situation. With all of the mind power I possessed I was able to stop the car from landing in the ocean. Instead, I steered the car across the water to the other side where we landed with a thud, on a grassy slope. The official looked at me with pure disbelief. He asked, "God, how did you do that?" I answered him, "By the power of my mind. I did not do this only for myself. When I realized that I didn't want either of us to die, it was almost too late. I did the only thing I could to stop it from happening. You can get out of the car now. I've removed the seal so the door will open. You will find your car at the first airport I locate."

The man opened his door. He fell down on his knees to the grass on the ground of the slope. He prayed for God's forgiveness and then he asked me to forgive him. He looked up at me and said, "How can I ever make this up to you?" I quickly replied, "By telling our President to believe in me and to act on the bombs in North Korea before it's too late."

The Beast

G od crept into my life like a thief in the night. I feel
utterly lost without communicating to him. I find
myself talking to him several times each day. I am often
depressed and tearful after dreaming of a prophecy. At times,
the prophecy dreams simply overwhelm me. I asked God
to space the intervals as He sent me the dreams of the Bible
prophecies. I explained to him that I just needed some time
to better myself both physically and mentally.

I became more involved each day as I wrote the book.
Three months passed without another prophecy dream.
This caused me to believe that I had received all of the
dreams intended for the contents of the book. One evening
as I realized my book was near completion, I asked God to
send any messages that He might still have for the book so
that I could go ahead and finish it. A few days later, I found
myself crawling into bed at one o'clock in the morning. I'd
spent the entire day and night writing the book. I tucked
myself into bed and said my prayers. Following my prayers
I began to talk to God. I told Him that if He had any more
quotations to send me in story form, tonight was as good
as any other to send. I was exhausted and immediately fell
asleep. I began dreaming. Of all the dreams, the following is
the most bazaar.

My daughter, Susan had just changed jobs in the government. Susan had taken a management position that required two months of schooling at the University of Nevada Reno. Susan and I decided that she and my grandson, Chance, would stay in my home until she could find a suitable two-bedroom apartment.

Susan and Chance arrived in Reno on the first day of July. Shortly thereafter, Susan found an apartment. The apartment was completely furnished and conveniently near the campus however, this area of the town was definitely not one of the safest areas.

I took care of Chance Monday through Friday. Susan came to pick him up at five o'clock each afternoon. I was glad to spend this time with my grandson and also to have Saturdays and Sundays to myself. I spent the weekends accomplishing the things I felt needed to be done.

After residing in Reno for six weeks, Susan called me on a Saturday asking me to watch Chance. She explained that she had forgotten something she needed for dinner at the grocery store and Chance was not awake from his late nap. I told Susan I'd be over after I left a note for Betty. Betty was not home from work and I wanted her to come to Susan's so we could all eat together.

I walked into the corridor of the apartment building and found the sign listing each tenants apartment number. Susan was in apartment sixteen. I was uneasy the moment I saw the number six. Six is a satanic number. However, the one in front of the six totaled seven. Seven is a spiritual number and in the end would override the six. Seven would protect Chance and Susan until she completed her schooling. I did not like the apartment and felt the sooner she left the better.

As I found apartment sixteen, my daughter was saying good-bye to a woman who was rising off of the white, pillowed couch. The woman had dark hair and skin. Her attire consisted of a short, black cotton dress, black stockings, black shoes and a black purse, which was still sitting on the floor. The dress was definitely too short to wear in public. After she left, I said, "I do not like that woman Susan. What did she want?" Susan replied, "Oh, for Heaven's sake Mom! The apartment serves my purpose well. The best qualities are the kitchen because of it's windows. I have a glass enclosed porch to hold the washer and dryer. And, the porch has plenty of shelves to make up for the ones not allowed in the kitchen because of the windows." "Susan!" I said, "I'm glad you're happy with the apartment. That's just fine but who was that woman?" Susan rolled her eyes at me and said, "Are we back on that again Mother? She was just a saleswoman trying to make a living just like the rest of us. She seemed perfectly nice to me. Subject closed. Now, for dinner; I should be back from the store within the hour. Do you want baked potatoes?"

I told Susan I didn't want potatoes. I only wanted some salad and a little meat because my appetite seemed to have suddenly vanished. Susan did return from the store within the hour. When she arrived I was standing at the sink, washing the ingredients for the salad.

The apartment's living room was in the shape of an L. I could see the television set from where I stood at the sink. It was off for a change. The television was always on when my grandson was awake, tuned to cartoons. I walked to the door directly in front of the television. I knew the set was off but as I started through the door, I felt waves coming from the screen. I grasped both sides of the doorframe.

Susan was headed from the living room to the kitchen when she saw me holding onto the doorframe. I heard her say, "Mom, are you having one of your dizzy spells? You haven't eaten today, have you?" I steadied myself and replied, "No, I'm fine. It just felt like something was coming out of the TV set, like waves of power." Annoyance was in Susan's voice as she said, "Good Lord! Mother, the TV set is not even on. You're being over dramatic, that's all!

The salad was prepared and chilling in the refrigerator. I would be done with my part of dinner after I ran water in the garbage disposal. Then, I could go into the living room and try to relax. I was glad to have this chance to get away from my daughter. "Nothing," I said, "is right!" I turned and started through the opening of the door. Again, I received the wave from the television set. This time it was so strong, it knocked me backwards. I lost my balance and almost fell to the floor. I yelled, "Susan, unplug that TV set now!"

Instead of turning in the direction of the television, Susan headed for the door. Betty had just arrived for dinner and Susan was letting her in. They began to chat about the events. I heard Betty ask, "Whose black purse is this sitting on the floor by the couch?" Susan replied, "What purse? Oh dear, that dark woman, that was here earlier, must have left her purse."

The dark woman, the dark purse and the waves from the television set all clicked together in my head. I felt as if a bomb had exploded in my head. Screaming, I ran through the door. The waves almost blew me over. I yelled, "Don't touch that purse! Get away from it!" Betty was already bending over for it and said, "It should have her address in it. Possibly even her phone number." "No! No! Don't touch it! Put that purse down!" I screamed. Betty replied, "But I can see a large sum of money inside of it. It should be returned to her. I don't see why I shouldn't go inside of it. It will tell us, at least, where she lives." I was running around the corner portion of the L-shaped room yelling, "Don't open that purse! Put it down! Don't open it!" I ran past Susan and halfway made it back to the kitchen when she asked, "Have you lost all of your senses? It's only a purse." Angrily, I retorted, "That purse is evil and an evil thing left it here on purpose."

I reached Betty right after she had turned one of the end-table lamps on. I pleaded, "Don't open it!" But, Betty had already opened it. As she turned to place it back on the floor, the purse fell open and two oblong shaped, black and gray, shells dropped out. They resembled oyster shells that had not yet been opened. The background was filled with strange sounds coming from the TV set. For the first time, Susan acted as if something might be wrong. I told Betty to get down on the floor next to the side of the couch by the door. I told Susan to do the same.

I bent down and said, "I'll take these unopened shells to the garbage disposal and get rid of them." I began walking to the kitchen holding a shell in each hand. Susan raced to me from behind and said, "No, you can't put them down the garbage disposal. They'll wreck it and I'll have to pay to have it fixed." I replied, "Well, better the garbage disposal than our lives." Susan said, "If one of us is going to dispose them, I will. Give them to me." I responded with an orderly tone, "No. Go back and huddle yourself behind the safety of the couch. Go now. Susan, don't argue with me!" As she was leaving she bumped me with her shoulder. I dropped both of the shells onto the tiled counter. They broke open and released an unknown black matter. It eased out, becoming larger and larger.

"Mother," Susan screamed, "there's a beast's face on the television!" I picked up one of the padded steel breakfast chairs and threw it at the screen. The glass shattered and the beast was gone. I shouted, "Betty stay down! Don't either of you move. Stay down no matter what you see or hear. Whatever you do, stay down! Turn the lights off and keep them off." I walked back into the kitchen intending to chop the black matter into pieces, put the pieces in the garbage disposal and rid the Earth of them, forever.

I grabbed a knife and cut into the first matter. As I cut it, the face of an animal appeared. The head was quite large but the body was not in proportion. It was much smaller and it appeared to have a long tail. It looked like a lion without the shaggy hair surrounding the face. I took the long butcher knife and swung at the animal. The face of the lion changed to that of a Japanese warrior. The eyes were black and slanted. His hair was neck length, black and straight. Above his upper lip was a thin, long black mustache. He was floating in front of the windows, high above my head. The face of this Japanese warrior was circling around me when I went to dispose of the other matter. The moment I touched the other matter it formed the shape of a lion. The face was the same as the other, the body smaller. It also floated toward the windows, high in the air above my head. The matter of the Japanese warrior changed itself back to the face of a lion. Now, there were two heads of a beast circling above me.

I heard Betty and Susan in the background. They were trying to comfort each other. I thanked God that Chance was still asleep in his bedroom. He was much safer that way. I could hear Susan softly crying. I always protected my children and grandchildren therefore I did not want her to be afraid as she witnessed this horrific situation. Somehow I would destroy these evil beasts.

I had not yet touched the other black matter. It was on the counter in the same place it had landed. I had to get the beasts out of this apartment. In order to do this I would have to trick them out of the door. In the time it took for me to blink my eyes these awful things could transform themselves, back and forth, from beasts to Japanese warriors. I knew I was not going to win this battle with the mere butcher knife I had gripped so tightly in my hand. I threw the knife onto the counter. The knife sliced off the corner of the black matter that had laid untouched on the counter. To my horror, the matter began to melt; transforming itself into another beast. This beast's face resembled the face of a calf. I had no more than seen the new beast before it became a Japanese warrior holding a sword in it's hand. If I did not take immediate action against these sinful creatures we would all be dead.

Instantly, my body shrunk in size and flew through the glass window above the counter. The beasts followed me. Armed with swords, they circled through the air in my direction. Each accompanied with malice intent to inflict pain or death upon me. I flew back through the window. The moment I was inside of the kitchen, a blue shield orbited the entire apartment. There is nothing that can penetrate an armored blue shield.

I watched the evil creatures in life form trying to break through the barrier of protection around the apartment. The blue shield thickened each time their attempts to re-enter the building became more vigorous. They gave up after many attempts. Instead, they began to attack the people walking on the street below the building. They were like a human form of vultures, swooping down to attack their enemy. The only difference being that they preyed victims, which were still alive.

A mother who had just come out of the butcher market with her small daughter in hand was pierced in the back with a sword from one of the Japanese warriors. A man got out his gray car to help the wounded woman lying on the sidewalk and the sobbing little girl huddling beside her. The tall, elderly man with gray hair left his car parked on the side of the street. His wife was in the front seat and his two grandchildren were in the back seat of the car. He told his wife to lock the doors and keep the windows closed and no matter what they saw, to stay inside of the car. He turned and headed in the direction of the woman wearing the blood-soaked brown, tweed coat. The man had not taken ten steps toward the unconscious woman when the swinging sword of a Japanese warrior punctured him. The other Japanese warriors swooped down to attack the man's gray car and the terrified family seated inside.

The afternoon was giving way to evening. The streets were becoming quite dark. The dim bulbs in the street lamps provided the only source of light. The cloak of darkness gave some form of protection to the helpless people in the streets. I could no longer bear to stand-by and watch these innocent men, women and children be slaughtered. I took to the air, protected only by the darkness. A man and boy were being attacked by one of the Japanese warriors. I flew straight down to the warrior. He did not expect anything to come down on him so the force of my hit knocked him to the ground. As he fell, I grabbed the sword out of his right hand.

One of the Japanese warriors was still attacking the gray car. He wanted the boy and girl sitting in the back seat so he was trying to break the rear window of the car. The hysterical screams coming from the woman and children inside the car could be heard a full street block away. With my sword prepared to attack, I flew toward the Japanese warrior. I severed his right arm and half of his shoulder. His sword dropped out of his right hand as his body slid down the back of the car. He had a shocked expression on his face when he landed in the street beside the curb. Gutter water flowed over his body.

This left one Japanese warrior to contend with. He was after me; flying at my heels. I glanced down and saw the innocent victims in the street running as fast as they could to the safety of their homes. I felt the blow of his blade slicing down the side of my face. My shirt was being soaked with the blood flowing from the gash on my face. I would surely be dead in moments, I thought. I prayed to God. I asked Him to forgive all of my sins.

I felt God's presence on the hand I was holding the sword in. My sword began glowing like a cold blue flame. I felt my arm move into the air, high above my head. The force of strength swinging the blade of the sword was a force that I've never known before. The hand of God aided me as I struck and decapitated the last evil Japanese warrior.

I felt such relief rush through my body. At last, the people were safe. They could continue their lives until the hour God called them up to Him. I touched my cheek to see if blood was still gushing out. I discovered my cheek completely healed.

When I awoke from this dream, I fully believed that I was going insane. I picked up the phone and dialed my friend Laverne's phone number. I explained my dream to her in full detail. As always, she calmly quoted the scripture from the Bible, which my dream prophesied – the war with the beast, the war of Armageddon.

The Angels will come down from the Heavens to join God as He battles Satin in the final war.

John the Prophet had dreams very similar to mine. This came from the Bible in the Book of Revelations. I hope as you read this you will realize that we are living in the final days of the world, as we know it.

Quotation from
"The Book Of Revelation"

The dream of Prophet John the Divine

A nd before the throne there was a sea of glass like unto a crystal: and in the midst of the throne and around the throne were four beasts full of eyes – before and behind.

The first beast that of a lion, the second beast that of a calf, the third beast that of a man and the fourth beast a flying eagle –

Our Country Tis' Of Thee Will Stand Alone

T hree years ago I dreamt of floods. The floods came to be reality. I dreamt of an earthquake in Japan that also came to be. During this period of time, I dreamt of a huge saw. The saw was as large as four thousand square feet. It sliced America away from the other countries in our world. The saw left a cut so deep that it was impossible to see the bottom of it and the width of the cut was so wide that no one could possibly cross it.

Cars had fallen into the wide gap and some of them could still be seen. Those cars, which could be seen, had landed in a cross and remained in that position because the earth's margin had stopped them from falling into the black hole of nothingness. Many people were determined to cross the cut. All who tried failed. Their screams could be heard throughout their fall into pit of blackness.

I spent a long time thinking about this dream. Eventually, I dismissed it. It was not long after the dream when our air bases began to shut down. This left our country with few soldiers to defend us. If Sadaam Hussein had called our bluff (the threat to send more troops over) than in all truth, we would have had no soldiers to send. The war in Iran is not over, it has not been finished. The Iranians are waiting to join forces with a large country such as Russia, Iraq or even China for their attack.

Now, several years later, we are once again closing airbases. This is the worst thing the government could do to our country. We are not replacing the soldiers that die in battles against other countries. This makes our country wide open for any attack which is coming our way. The split in the ground which will separate our country for others means we will have an open war and there will not be a single country to step in and help us fight. We will fight our war alone and we will most assuredly lose.

War In Our Own Country

I worked late into the evening knowing that tomorrow would be a full day. It is the day of my daughter Susan's wedding and it is a three-hour journey away. I knew that there would be a lot to do in a very little amount of time. It was a spur of the moment decision between Susan and her fiancé.

I had the feeling that time was running out for everyone, our world in such a terrible economic condition. There are wars and memories of wars and the Bible's prophecies are being fulfilled at a rapid pace. Inwardly, we all wonder just how long it will be until we see fighting in our own land.

It was late in the night when I finally retired to my bed. I restlessly dozed throughout the night. When I did sleep the dream was there.

I awoke early the next morning. All of my suitcases were packed and I put them into the car after I ate breakfast. I looked around the house. For some reason I felt it would be the last time I would ever see it. I started the three-hour journey to Susan's home not knowing why I felt this way.

I arrived at her home around noon. The house looked as if it were well preserved. The forest background spread ten miles in each direction. It was a perfect setting to raise a child, have a home, to find love and to be loved. The house set back half a mile from the main road. A winding gravel road led to Susan's home. I bounded around the curves paying little heed to the car's protesting. It bumped up and down on the road as the house came into view.

The house sat in a clearing. The forest had an assortment of Juniper, Pine, Fir, and Cedar trees that looked like Christmas trees, all growing in mass confusion. A circle driveway was in the front of the house. There was a cedar tree to the left of the porch and one to the right. They gave the house a homey feeling. The house was in good condition. The roof and the porch were two different shades of green. The sides of the house were white. Somehow, it seemed the house just blended in with the forest and this made it difficult to see even though it was in plain view.

I knew there was much to be done so I bounded from the car to the stairway leading to the porch. The front door was open. I walked in and called for Susan but she was nowhere to be found. I heard someone upstairs so I called for her again. This time she came down. She said to me, "Mom, we have a lot to do and not much time to do it in, so let's get busy." I nodded my head in full agreement. Family and friends would soon be arriving to enjoy the occasion so; she began cleaning the house in the living room.

I started in the kitchen with the making of the salad. I also laid out everything needed to set the table. Several hours before the wedding was to begin almost everything was prepared. I wanted this wedding to be very successful because I knew it would be my daughter's last. I liked Pat, the man she was going to marry. He seemed to take to my grandson and would be a good father for him. I felt this within my heart.

As the day wore on, I discovered that the windows had locked shutters. They remained locked when I tried to open them. I asked my daughter, "Susan, why do you have the house all shuttered up? We are working almost in complete darkness." She looked at me and said, "Mom, I didn't put the shutters on the windows. I've been so busy that I didn't notice they were closed or that they were locked. You're right. It is to dark in here." We tried to unlock the shutter but were unable to. There seemed to be an invisible lock that neither of us could find. The windows remained closed, leaving the rooms of the house in darkness. I said, "Susan do you have any candles or kerosene lamps we might use? Today is supposed to be a joyous occasion, full of light and laughter and the only inkling that the day is bright and shiny is coming from the sunbeams creeping through the lattice." I tried not to let the dimness of the light bother me.

The time was getting near and everything was prepared. My son arrived with his three children and my sister Ev. This pretty well completed the family and friends that would be attending the evening's celebration of the wedding. My son settled the children down and came in to visit with me. The food was ready and set out on the tables. The wedding ceremony was to be within an hour. Susan had gone upstairs to dress. I visited momentarily with my son. I tried to find a spot inside the darkened house that would give a ray of light to the wedding and give it some indication of a celebration. I looked around and found nothing. With the setting of the sun the house was growing even darker.

I asked my son to take the children to pick some fall leaves or dried flowers to make the occasion more festive. He and the children exited through the back door to look in the distant fields. Fall was upon us and the evening was already getting chilled. I heard someone behind me. When I turned around to say something I saw my father, Harvey standing there. I was so shocked that I dropped the spoon I was holding in my hand. He had been dead for twenty years. I walked up to him and said, "Are you real?" He replied, "For this time, I am real. I have come to lead you and your family to safety." I asked him what the danger he felt was. He said, "Daughter, haven't you noticed that the shutters have been sealed closed?" "Yes, I have but I wasn't aware that it was you who closed them." I continued by telling him that it was almost time for the wedding. He said, "No child, this wedding cannot be because there is not time for it." Surprised, I said, "But we've worked all day on this. It's just barely thirty minutes away. Surely whatever is going on can wait until then." My father pointed toward the shutters. The sun was setting. He said, "Come with me daughter but tell no one else. I want you to see the sight for yourself and then you can tell me if there is time for the wedding."

I walked over to the window he was standing at. When I looked through the shutters I saw the most horrifying sight. It was a sight to behold. There were huge red clouds that reached completely down to the ground and went several hundred feet into the air. A reddish color was lit by the evening sun. It looked like the whole world was on fire. Puzzled, I looked toward my father and said, "What is it I see?" My father replied, "Those are bombs you see daughter, atomic bombs." I looked again to make sure it was truly so. The whole world seemed to be covered with a reddish colored, dusty film. He said, "Tell me now daughter, is there time?" I answered, "But, if the bombs are already exploded, can't we take the time to perform the ceremony? Please let Susan have this." He shook his head no and said, "This cannot be, there is not time."

Suddenly, a man came from under ground. He walked up the porch stairs and into the room. The man said, "It is time to go now Harvey, now." I'd never, in my life, seen this man before nor was he introduced to me. I just knew he was there and that he was speaking to my father. My father was as real as life and so was the man.

I was bewildered and puzzled as Susan burst into the room. Her husband to be was standing in the corner and his face lit up and beamed when he saw her standing there but neither saw my father. And my father said to me, "Go and tell her that there is not time for the wedding because the enemy is near." I said to him, "That could not be because I saw nothing but the golden clouds mixed with the sun to make a burnished orange red. The whole world itself seemed to be on fire." My father became very stern and he said, "Daughter, go and get your son because we must leave immediately." My daughter seeing my father for the first time asked, "Who are you?" And please not now." He replied, "I am your grandfather Harvey, I am your son's guardian angel. I have come for the both of you and the time is now because the enemy is approaching upon us now. We must flee if we are to save our lives." My daughter suddenly turned and saw her son coming down the hallway. She ran to him and picked him up in her arms. My father walked over to Susan, took my grandson, Chance, and carried him to the door. He turned back once and said to her, "Follow me Susan because I will lead you to safety, I will lead you to God."

By that time, my son was very alarmed. He walked into the room with his three children and my sister Ev. He asked, "What's going on?" Again, my father explained that the enemy is very near. My son walked to the door, looked out and became horrified with what he saw. He looked at me for hope and guidance. I said, "Son, take these children and my sister. She will help you to guide and guard them. Take them to safety, go to the car that you have hidden in the forest and leave by the north road that leads up into the mountains. You must go in one direction and your grandfather, Susan and Chance must go in another. At the end of the road, the pathways will meet and all of you will be together again." My father said to me, "Remain here daughter. You will see the enemy approaching. You will know when the time is right and at that time, you will disappear."

I waited for more than an hour. I sat and I paced the floor. I prayed this could not be happening. I could hear shrubs and brush outside as someone moved through them. It was very dark. I calmed my fears and I opened the front door. I wanted to see outside and what was coming for me. In the gullies and in the shadows of the trees, I saw the enemy approaching. Some crawled on their hands and knees, some were going from tree to tree. Some hid behind anything they could find to hide behind. Some had already reached the barn. I was shocked to see this. I could see them clearly. The face of the enemy were that of Japanese and some looked as though they might be North Korean. It was too dark to see plainly. However, I saw that they were dressed in dark green kaki pants and jackets. They wore helmets, which almost matched, and had blotches of camouflage attached to their clothing so that they would not be seen. They also wore dark brown high top boots that laced right up to the mid-calf of their legs. They carried machine guns and pistols.

I knew that it was just a matter of seconds before they would surround the house. I looked in the direction my children and my father had taken toward the mountains. They were no longer in sight. It was as if the darkness had swallowed them up. But for some reason, my inner voice told me that they would be all right. I heard the front door rattle. Even though the front door was locked I knew it was merely a matter of time until they would break the door and enter the house. I also heard movement from the south side of the house. This meant that in only moments they would be coming up on the back porch and the stairs that led in either direction. Why was it I must stay after everyone else was gone, I questioned myself? I heard the surround the building and then come inside. I went up the stairs as fast as I could. I knew that my inner voice would tell me what to do from here on out.

I could hear them as they silently and steadily climbed the stairway. I knew that "my time" the time my father had spoken of had come. I went to the window, opened it and walked out upon the higher balcony that led from the bedroom door. I looked down at the house and down at the men. I knew the house in which Susan had lived would be no more. Suddenly, I realized that I was flying through the air, toward the direction of safety. I knew that the time in this world was at it's end. I knew that my father had come to get my family and he had chosen the pathway that would safely lead them to God. I went in that direction; hoping that God would accept me with open arms, as I knew He had accepted them. I knew my job on this earth was finished and that my new life was ready to begin. As I neared the clouds, they broke apart into a million shades of pink with the tinge of lavender. I knew I was heading in the direction of God.

After that, I woke with a start. All through the next day, I was sad and pondered about what I should do about this prophecy. How could I tell people, who would believe me? Would anyone ever believe that our own country will be bombed? Or, that the enemy would be burning our homes to the ground. That the world and the sky would be on fire from the bombs. Who, in this lifetime, would believe me when it was only a prophecy, a dream? I tell all of you who will now listen, this prophecy will come true. We need to be aware that the anti-christ is present in our lives and has been for quite some time. He is a government official. I am in full agreement with Nostradamus in regards to this person's name containing the letter B. When you read this and hear this, know that the time is near and prepare yourself for God and for your journey into the mountains, up into the Heavens to be with Him unto all eternity.

Prelude to Journey to the Mountains

G od had a plan for me. I left Reno and moved into the high mountains. Over the next three years, I gained incredible knowledge of the spiritual world. It was the perfect place. Fur trees covered the high mountains and had a view from every window. At night, I sat on my deck and listened to the small streams run through the property into the larger streams. The knowledge I gained in the spiritual world was incredible. My spiritual doves and I were under attack on many occasions but they protected me each time. Just as I knew it was time to go to the mountains, I knew my time in the mountains was over so I sold my home and returned to Reno.

Many years had passed since I'd had a dream of prophecy. I had lived in Reno for nearly three years and I began to wonder if the last prophecy would come to me before my death. In the month of my birth, September, the last prophecy came to me. It is fitting it arrived in the ninth month as nines represent houses, dwellings and marriage.

In the past months, there has been an eruption of spirits that have come to guard me. They know about the book and have come to protect me while I finish it. There is an urgency to their presence. They are not the only ones who know about the book. You see, I have been trying to tape the end of the book so I can get it published. Mysterious things would happen to the tapes such as loud thumps that would sound out my voice when I recorded certain subjects. After two tape recorders and hours upon hours of taping (and frustration I might add) I gave up and hand wrote the rest of the book.

I prayed to my Lord Jesus to protect me and the publishing of this book. It has been eight years now and the doves which I know now were sent for my protection, are still with me, they go everywhere I go and I am never without them. I'm fairly sure they'll remain by my side until the end. They are quite simply awesome and sometimes at night I see them as angels. There are ten doves that guard me now and additional spirits, mainly older men. Sometimes at night, they sit in the chair beside my bed and sometimes they hover near the ceiling. There is a man in logger's clothes that stands by my bed and I know he will play an important part in my future on the next plain. I am protected where ever I go making privacy a thing of the past, I am of course, grateful to the Lord for this protection. The spirit Matthew stayed with me for five months. He was as real as you are to me. I was so happy having him with me, happier than I'd been in years. Every time I thought of him leaving I would begin sobbing as we had become so close in the mountains. There is another spirit, Santiago, who became quite jealous of Matthew and eventually, took him away. When I was trying to record the book certain sections of my time with Matthew would be erased and the part where I would travel up with Matthew and marry Santiago would be left. I began crying each time I had to re-record the section where Matthew is taken away from me. It has been quite emotional for me on all planes. I have waited half a lifetime to meet Santiago and now I find I don't like him. He is arrogant and selfish and tramples over anyone who gets in his way, including Matthew. Santiago and I were married in another life and have a son together. I will love my son and do whatever I can to help him. However, I know that Santiago is only interested in my dawry and he is truly in love with his mistress. I've been told that I'm a high priestess on the next plane and that this dawry is very large.

As I've said before, my dreams wear me out because I'm experiencing everything as if it is really happening. I awake with stiff legs and sore feet. Sometimes I am so tired it is exhausting to climb the flight of stairs in my current home. Spirits are constantly coming, one after the other, telling me to hurry up and finish the book. It is mind boggling in itself (to say the least) that they know about the book but they do. This book seems to have some significance to the people on a higher plane. They certainly know me. Since writing this sequence of the book I have learned my heavenly name is Gracelyn.

Let us all realize that when the time described in the next section comes it will bring difficult choices for all. It could bring hardship along the way, but if you want to survive it can be done. Our fore fathers went through just such hardships and much more than we've experienced in our time. They survived by carving their homes out of the wilderness. The bible in hand on Sundays was the only day of rest. They lived because they were willing to try and you will succeed with that same frame of mind. It will not be easy for us but we have the same courage and stamina as our fore fathers had. The one thing I know is you must keep God close in your heart. He will give you the strength to see it through.

We will all probably start from the beginning, but just remember how the story unfolds. How these people began again. They survived in those mountains because they were willing to help one another. It wasn't a this is mine and this is yours situation, they were willing to share and share alike. The love story will unfold in your life as it did for Gracelyn. I dreamt these dreams to show us how to find safety in the end. You will be just as safe if you listen to your inner voice and no one else's. Help one another and God will help you. He'll tell you where to go and what to do when you get there. The higher the elevation you go, the safer you will be. This world will be destroyed in certain places similar to a natural disaster. One house will be destroyed and another left standing. Cash money will see you through just as it saw us through before. Get rid of your credit cards as they are the mark of the beast.

This is the last prophecy I will receive. Once the book is on the market, the doves will go up with me. I have always said and firmly believe what is with us in this world will be part of our eternity. Wish me luck up there as I think I'm going to need it . . . after all, all lives have hardships. I know a beautiful adventure awaits me.

Please remember to listen to your inner voice and not someone else. You are the only one that can hear it and it is always the right answer. The chills have always told me when I'm correct and I have had chills with every sentence of this next section Now, sit back and enjoy the last prophecy as you discover where to go for safety.

Ev grabbed my arm and said, "I'm getting hungry. Let's go." I replied, "I can't go until I hear what he's saying. It's important because I'm chilled to the bone. Go on without me. I'll walk home." I couldn't leave because whenever I'm chilled like this it has something to do with a prophecy and I didn't live more than a ten minute walk from here. Ev went on. From that moment on, the old man didn't take his eyes off of me. It was as if he were talking only to me. The wind came up and was quite chilly but nothing compared to how cold my body was. I looked up and saw dark clouds hovering in the sky. It was almost cold enough to snow. What happened to our beautiful fall day I wondered. The crowd began to leave and in minutes only a dozen or so remained. Soon I was the only person left. I held my silence and allowed him to speak directly to me. His words left me speechless. Sell your belongings for cash. "Keep only your blankets and sturdy clothing," he said. I had spent half a lifetime acquiring my beautiful furniture and I was becoming irritated with his words. I told him he must be mistaken, the time isn't here yet. I didn't realize that the sun had come out again, the wind had died down and it was as warm as it had been earlier. I was still freezing and he seemed to know it. "You are one of us. Your chills, as you already know, come to you for a reason. Gracelyn, go and tell everyone you can to prepare to journey into the mountains within two days. Make sure you are with them," he said. I replied, "You must have the wrong person. My name is not Gracelyn, it's Joyce." "Remember only the clothes and money are important. Choose your clothing wisely. Do as I say and you and your sister will be safe. Go and tell her now. Start preparing yourself," the old man said. I glanced over my shoulder to see if my sister had returned, wondering how he'd known that she was my sister in the first place since we don't look alike. When I turned back to ask him, he had vanished.

It took a lot for me to sell my belongings. The things I had each had a significant meaning to me. But, I knew the old man was right because when his words ran through my mind, I became chilled to the bone. It wasn't easy to convince my sister but she also knew that my chills were something of an omen.

My sister and I stood in line together with our bundles on the ground in front of us. Panic rushed through me when I realized I had accidently left my bag of money in my dresser drawer. I told her to just stay in line. She would be just fine until I returned as some of my friends were also in line. I was going back for the money and I'd return. There were so many people in line; four across and at least two miles in front of us. I figured I had plenty of time as I headed as fast as I could across town. I placed my bag under the edge of a building which served as a grill and small bar. No one would bother with it because everyone in line appeared to already have more than they could handle.

When I reached the house that was no longer mine the door was unlocked. Every last piece of furniture was gone and so was my money bag. I couldn't believe everything had been removed so fast. In awe, I sat down on the step of the front porch. I put my head down between my legs and wondered what on earth was going to happen to me now. I don't know how long I sate there before I decide I must shake the depression which had descended on me off and move on. My legs were too tired to move but I knew they must. Losing my money was the last thing in the world I needed. Thoughts of being penniless and having to beg were almost more than I could bear. I got up and silently prayed as I returned to where I'd left my bundle. I prayed God would send me a miracle, unbeknownst to me, He already had.

It was late when I arrived back at the trail I was shocked to see I was alone. I had expected to see others making the journey as well but there was no one else. There was a stream that flowed into the Truckee River and a bar and grill had been built on a high foundation so the stream ran below it. A portion was glassed in but there was also a large deck that had accommodated the many people that ate there. I had last seen my friend Rob sitting on the deck pondering whether or not to continue up the mountain. I knew it would be best if he continued on and had he still been there I would've done my best to influence his decision. He was gone and so was the bundle he had been carrying. Now, I may never know what happened to him. If there was still a line when I made it to the top I would do my best to find him and hopefully we would join my sister in line. I was left entirely alone and on my own. I had literally wasted an entire day trying to retrieve my money bag. More important than the money were my two dogs. The dogs were no where to be found now. I hoped they had stayed with Ev. I worried about my older dog Cyndi. I had planned on carrying her in my bundle as she has arthritis in her hips and Fluffy would've walked next to me on a leash but they had run away in the confusion. The only consolation was that I knew if any dog could find his owner it was Fluffy.

Fluffy had crept through a small opening in my gate once when I was living in the mountains. I could hear him barking in the distance but it was as dark as an ace of spades without the light from a full moon to guide him home. It was so dark I was unable to see my finger in front of my face. I called for Fluffy over and over but I couldn't hear his little paws coming home. My inner voice told me to leave the back porch light on and leave the gate wide open. I had accomplished all I could possibly do and retired to bed. I prayed he would make it home on his own. Of course, sleep was impossible knowing he was out there all alone. I waited and listened. Around one thirty in the morning my voice told me to go to the door. I was so ecstatic to see him wandering on the porch waiting to be let in that I didn't even scold him. So I knew if it were possible to find me, Fluffy would and Cyndi would follow him. With that positive thought, I began my long journey up the mountain.

Under normal circumstances I'd let my inner voice lead me as it was never wrong when I followed it but I figured there was bound to be many tracks left behind by the people that had gone before me. I started on the trail determined to find my sister and all of the other people. I glanced up at the sun and decided from it's position the time must be between two or half past. This meant I would have to hustle as there was no chance of arriving at my destination before night fall and I'd have to find a safe place to spend the night. I did have one advantage though. I was a fast walker and the trail was clear of people and there didn't appear to be any obstacles on the trail. Except, what was that? Could it be a man walking towards me? It was, a tall dark man coming towards me. His clothes looked familiar. He had a red and black long sleeved shirt on and black pants which were belted at the waist. As he came closer, I saw the shirt was checkered. Now I was positive that at some point in time I had seen this man before. He walked straight up to me and said, "Well, I suppose you're the stragler I was sent back here to find. What's the matter with you? Couldn't you keep up with the others? And do you really expect to make it all of the way to the settlement with that large bundle?" Flabbergasted with his sarcastic tones, I replied "Let me tell you something; I can't find my sister or my friend Rob and I've lost all of my money and both of my dogs!" I swung my bundle onto my back so hard I nearly knocked myself onto the ground but I regained my balance and took off leaving him in the dust. It wasn't long before he caught up with me. I simply ignored his presence. His stride was much larger than mine and even with the freedom of my jeans and comfortable shoes my short legs were just no match to his. As I pondered the situation I decided it was ridiculous for me to try to kill myself with such a fast pace for the likes of him. My pace slowed within the second mile. I knew without a doubt I had seen this man before but I just couldn't place him. My bundle was becoming a burden. The only way to carry such a load was to put it around your neck and let it hang down your back. I had already lost more than I wanted to recall and knew I simply had to carry on. I asked myself, "Could it get any worse?" Ever so often I would put my bundle down to readjust it and hope by some miracle that when I turned around my dogs would be following me. The dogs weren't there this time either and as I tried to figure out what was jabbing me in the shoulder I heard the man ask if I was having some kind of problem. Irritated, I replied, "As a matter of fact, I am. Something is jabbing me and I'm trying to fix it." "Well do it and let's go. I've got better things to do." he said.

It seemed hours had passed before we slowed down again. All of a sudden he stopped and stood still as if he were listening for something or maybe (I prayed) he was trying to recall a safe place for us to rest. I was thoroughly exhausted and needed to give my back a rest. I had a blister on my left foot. I decided anyplace would be fine to rest so I removed my bundle and plopped myself onto the dirt in the middle of the trail. I stretched realizing every part of my body ached. Now, I hate whiners and since I had partially created my own dilemma I didn't want to become one but I knew if I didn't rest I would fall over in my tracks unable to continue at all. I could tell by the look on his face he wasn't pleased with me. He made his way to the left of the road. I hoped he was searching for a safe place for us to rest. Then, a tad bit embarrassed with myself, I realized he probably just needed some privacy. There was a cool breeze and it felt wonderful. It was actually a bit chilly but the elevation was higher than I was used to and fall temperatures came earlier up here. The man had been gone for a while now and I decided I should probably get up and prepare myself to continue on. I could hardly lift myself up off of the ground. As I tried to situate myself, I saw them, fresh wagon wheel tracks! I knew my sister, Ev (short for Evelyn) must be close. The day had taken it's toll on me and I had tears in my eyes. I felt alone and helpless but the fresh tracks lifted my spirits a bit.

Where was the man? The boulders and brush he had disappeared into made it difficult for a person to get through and a wagon could never pass through. My thoughts were so involved in my dilemma I hadn't noticed until now that the sun was disappearing behind the tall trees that covered the mountain. Damn that man, didn't he realize how awful I felt? Just as I decided I would begin to look for him, there he was. My mouth fell open as I saw him appear from behind a ten foot boulder. He was clean from head to toe and his clothes were fresh. The closer he came the angrier I got. Did he think he was the only person that needed to clean up? It was enough to make a saint swear! My hair was covered in dirt and mixed with sweat, my clothes were filthy and my legs and feet still ached. Not to mention that because of my own vanity my face was red from the sunburn I'd acquired during this awful day. You see, I have a small head and if I did wear a hat it was a child's hat. They made me look stupid so I didn't even think about bringing one with me.

I was really angry now and I was determined to find the water he had been in even if it took me all night. I breezed past him without even one word. I made it past the boulders and found a deer trail that made it's way to another section of boulders. I carefully edged around them and saw a small clearance, maybe twenty five feet, in the forest of large green fur trees. The air smelled like Christmas. There was water and it shimmered as the last of the sun's rays filtered through the tree's limbs. As exhausted as I was it was impossible to ignore the beauty of the high mountains. I did not know where the man had gone but I knew this was where I intended to spend the night.

My plan to ease my pain in the water came to an abrupt halt once I emerged myself. It was freezing and I had already begun to shiver. I quickly rinsed my hair, scrubbed my body and my clothes. I raced out of the shallow pool of water taking half of it's sand with me. My teeth were chattering and I thought I had frozen my brain because I could smell the scent of coffee and bacon. Could the man be cooking I wondered. I realized now I was starving because I began to have stomach pains. First, I had to dry my clothes. There was a flat boulder, large enough to sleep two people and then some. The sun hadn't set yet so I ran over to lay out my clothes. I was in such a hurry to get to the rock I almost ran right into the man. "You just about scared me to death," I screamed, "Where did you come from?" The man replied, "I was waiting over by those rocks for you. Here, I've warmed this blanket by the fire for you." I nodded and I knew he knew I was gracious. I told him I was hungry. I hadn't had anything since very early that morning. "I know you are. I've prepared a bacon sandwich and some hot coffee for you. There's a blanket on the ground and the rocks will warm our backs. Come on Gracelyn." he said. "What did you call me? Gracelyn? You must have me confused. My name is Joyce." I said, a little confused myself. He shook his head, "No it's not. You are Gracelyn." he responded without a doubt in his voice. Frustrated, I called him overbearing and told him to have it his way. I was too hungry and cold to fight. I grabbed the sandwich and quickly returned to the flat boulder my clothes were drying on. The sun had disappeared leaving the boulder completely shaded. The breeze was chilling me to the bone. I could hear the fire crackling in the distance. Once again I thought that man could make even a saint swear. My teeth were chattering but before long I heard his footsteps approaching. I said nothing. I was too afraid my voice would betray me and I would start to cry. He stood in front of me and said, "I'm sorry. I know this must be hard on you. It's been hard on me. By the way, I'm Matthew. Night is upon us. Let's stay warm by the fire."

I don't even remember falling asleep. I just awoke sometime in the night to find Matthew asleep. He had wrapped his body around mine for warmth. He was sleeping so soundly, I didn't want to move and chance waking him up. He had a long grueling day and I felt I was to blame for that. We awoke at the same time in the morning. He surprised me by just laying there for a few minutes. To tell you the truth, I needed the rest and could have stayed there all day but, of course, this was not an option. I arose but the pain shooting through my legs was too much to bear. With tears welling up in my eyes I sat back down. Matthew helped me up again and held me until I was steady. He gently eased me forward, step by step. The blister on my left foot was throbbing worse than a toothache and caused me to hobble. Matthew could tell I would not be going anywhere in this condition and asked me what hurt the most. I told him it was my foot. He told me to sit back down on the rock which I gladly obeyed. He rubbed some kind of a solution onto my blister and then wrapped it with a piece of his shirt. Then, he pulled out a small leather pouch and removed a small white pill. He gestured me to open my mouth and placed the pill on my tongue. I swallowed it without much thought. I figured anything might help now. Within minutes all of my pain was gone. My legs no longer ached and my foot could bear weight again. "Why didn't I ask him for anything earlier?" I silently wondered.

We reached the settlement around noon that day. It was a huge fort. The perimeter had been surrounded with thick logs piled at least fifteen feet high. I could hear water raging. The water ran straight through the settlement. There was a long log bridge. The creases had been filled with smooth river rocks and sand so wagon wheels could easily pass over the bridge. As we crossed the bridge I saw numerous cabins. I felt like someone had been preparing this safe haven for quite some time. I guessed this property had at least a year of preparation invested in it. For some reason, this made me feel more secure. I said a silent prayer to my Lord Jesus for allowing my safe arrival and thanked him for sending Matthew for guidance. I knew without a doubt that this mysterious tall dark man had saved me. Someday soon I would find a way to properly thank him.

My mind began racing with questions. Was my sister in one of these cabins? Had she arrived here safely? How was I going to find her? Then I began to worry. It was all I could do to get her to trust me enough to follow the trail. Had she gone to the left instead of the right on the trail? Had anyone shown her the way like Matthew had for me? Where was Matthew I wondered? I would describe her to him and see if he knew where she was. My sister, Ev, was all I had now. For years we had lived within minutes of each other but a few years earlier she had moved away to be near her daughter. Oddly enough, she was visiting me when this all began. She had flown in for a quick visit before the cold winter set in. Luckily, Ev knew the weather and had brought plenty of warm comfortable clothes for her visit. Even in September the temperature is chilly. I needed my sister.

Just then I heard Matthew ask in a teasing manner what my hurry was? I began to see how handsome this man was when I turned around to answer him. Matthew had beautiful grey hair that curled at the ends. I never cared much for long hair on men but somehow his suited him. I asked, "Where should I go Matthew? I'm so exhausted I could fall over right here?" He pointed to the cabin in front of us and jokingly said, "Well, can you make it there or shall I carry you?" I ignored his last remark and began walking as fast as I could to the cabin. I could see a long log bench on the porch and couldn't wait to remove my shoes. There were cabins as far as the eye could see. Some were built of stone and logs and some with just logs. Each had a shingle roof and an East entrance. This allowed the afternoon sun to enter the sparingly placed windows and provided plenty of light. I liked that the glass windows each could be covered with wood shutters. The carpenters, whoever they were, were quite talented.

It felt good to know the first part of my journey was over. I was crazy to have gone back for my money. What had I been thinking? There wasn't enough money in the world to make it worth what I had gone through these last three days. My legs had begun to ache again. Matthew and I walked up the steps to the porch together. He sat my bundle down. I was so tired I hadn't realized I wasn't carrying it. Matthew told me to go inside. That my bedroom was to the left and on the counter I would find fresh water to wash with. He told me to put some fresh clothes on and he'd return to dress my blister. "Rest Gracelyn, you're home." Matthew said. I snapped back "My name is not Gracelyn, it's Joyce!" I was too tired too argue though. I needed to take these filthy clothes off, wash and lie down in my long white night gown I always wore to bed and just rest. My eyes rushed to the water bucket that sat on the wood plank counter. One bucket wasn't enough to clean me. My eyes wandered around the room. There was a back door. Slowly, I crossed the room and opened the door. I was grateful to find more water on the back porch. There was a wooden key barrel that was full of fresh water. I could hear water flowing swiftly over some rocks. It sounded like a waterfall. It was pleasant. There was a path which had a downwards slope. It curved around a huge boulder so tall in fact not even a goat could climb it. It added an extra layer of safety to my little cabin and I was happy it was part of my new back yard. Although my body ached I couldn't resist the urge to follow the path. Moments later I arrived at a pond! It was a waterfall I had heard. The water poured from the high mountains into the pond a down a small stream which joined other small streams making their way to a large rushing river. The pond must be thirty feet in diameter and maybe five feet deep. I could see large boulders at the bottom through the crystal clear water. I quickly removed every stitch of my clothing and jumped in. I gasped as the water was quite cold. The sun filtered through the large pine trees. The water was up to my neck as I sank down, just perfect. I wondered how long I would reside here. At that moment it didn't really matter I realized. This was the first time I had relaxed in so long. I soaked for ten minutes or so and then washed my face and hair. I quickly returned to the cabin feeling replenished from the cold water. I entered the cabin and walked the length of the room which served as the living room, dining room as well as the kitchen. There was a large rock fireplace between two doors. The fireplace went clear up to the ceiling. The two doors opened up to bedrooms. Matthew had put my bundle in the bedroom on the left. Although the water had replenished me I was quite weary. I found my white gown, slipped it over my head and decided it was time to lay down. There was a homemade bedspread made up of a variety of soft velvet squares. I spread myself out on top of it and was asleep before my head hit the pillow.

The sun streaming into the bedroom window awoke me. How long had I been asleep? I hurried to get dressed and flung the bedroom door open. Matthew was sitting at the table eating. He appeared rested and very clean. "Hi." I said, "I guess I slept longer than I had intended. I'm starving. Is there anymore food?" "Do you always start your mornings off with questions?" he asked. "Morning! You mean I slept all of yesterday afternoon and clear through the night?" I questioned, quite surprised. Matthew looked so refreshed and I still looked like death warmed over I thought. Fate was certainly more fair to men than women. "Gracelyn, there's food in the warming oven on the stove for you. I have a lot to catch up on so I'll be leaving shortly. Relax and rest today. You still look tired." Matthew said. "Why do you persist in calling me that name?" I asked. Matthew was already at the front door. He turned halfway around and said so softly I could barely him "Because it is your heavenly name. So, get used to it." And then he left.

I did what Matthew asked of me and rested, for a while, at least. I examined the cabin. It was well built. The thick logs would keep it warm in the winter and cool in the summer. The rock wall had a wooden folding clothes rack attached to it. The stove sat on a cement foundation with warming ovens on each side of the pipe. It had been designed with fire safety in mind. The stove reminded me of when I was a young bride. I lived on a ranch and had cooked for two weeks on a wood stove during a horrific snow storm. The storms were much more severe back then. It seemed like a thousand years has passed me since then. I realized I could take the water from the back porch and warm it on the stove this winter.

I decided I had several hours before Matthew returned. I might as well become acquainted with my new surroundings. There was a little room at the end of the kitchen. I opened the thick wood door to find a room with walls of solid stone. I propped the door open so I could see inside. There were wooden barrels on the shelf in the pantry filled with yeast, lard, sugar, salt, baking soda, baking powder, tea leaves and coffee. There was a trap door in the floor. I pulled it open with it's leather strap and found both sweet and white potatoes as well as a small shelf filled with several pounds of butter. It was as cold in there as a refrigerator. Whoever had stocked this pantry had thought of everything. It reminded me of the Morman religion. I always believed their religion had merit. I decided to try my hand at making yeast bread. By dusk I was again exhausted. I had spent the entire afternoon baking loaves of bread, rolls and last but not least a batch of oatmeal raisin cookies. The cookies were a treat for Matthew. It was the least I could do for him. But, in reality, they were for me too, sweets had always been my biggest weakness. Dusk slipped into the darkness of the night and still no Matthew. I had gone no further than the pond and didn't have a clue where to find him so I pushed the soup I'd prepared for dinner to the back of the stove and filled the fire box with more wood. Hopefully the soup would stay warm until he arrived.

Using the warm water from the holding bin, I washed myself. I removed my white gown from the back of the chair and slipped it over my head. I left a kerosene lamp burning on low on top of the warming oven and took another from the table and into my bedroom. Although I was exhausted I was restless listening for Matthew's footsteps on the front porch. Had he left for good? My heart thudded against my chest. I didn't know anyone else here. I didn't know if my sister had made it here safely. My mind wandered with worry until I drifted off. I'd forgotten to pull the shade so the first rays of sun immediately woke me. Still no Matthew. I paced back and forth through the cabin peeking out each window. I decided not to leave the cabin because I didn't want to chance missing him. Around noon I gathered our dirty clothes up into a wicker basket. I ran down to the pond of water to quickly wash them. If you didn't listen closely you would miss the birds singing in the trees because the waterfall was so loud. I soaked the clothes in the shallow area of the pond, rinsed them in the deeper area and laid them out in the bushes to dry. I was already here and figured I might as well properly bath myself.

The sun was beginning to set when I saw Matthew crossing the bridge. I had moved the rocking chair to the front window and sat there waiting. I was more than just a little angry, I had worked myself up into a full blown temper. No wonder I wanted nothing to do with men for so many years. The frustration they cause simply isn't worth it I thought. It had been years and years since I'd waited on a man. I left the rocker and retreated to my bedroom, closing the door behind me, before Matthew reached the front porch. There was a sick feeling in my stomach, I was frightened for my future and felt terribly alone. A few minutes later I heard a soft knock on the door. "Are you in there Gracelyn?" Matthew asked. I turned my face into the pillow so it would muffle my sobs. Yet another thing I hadn't done in years. I could no longer hold the tears in and I cried myself to sleep before the sun had fully set.

The smell of bacon awoke me. Obviously Matthew was up. I reached for a fresh pair of jeans and pulled a blue sweat shirt over my head. The mornings were quite chilly. I intended on exploring the settlement today. If my sister was here I would find her today even if it meant knocking on every cabin's door. I would move my things to her cabin before nightfall. I remained in my bedroom until I heard Matthew leave. He had set a place for me at the table, complete with a cloth napkin. I couldn't believe my eyes! The little bag I kept all of my money in was right there in the center of the plate! With the bag against my chest I thanked God. Than the guilt set in. I was so angry with him for leaving me that I never thought about what he might be doing. How had he found my bag? It was a nearly impossible task. He was a complex man but then, what man isn't? This is why I'd steered clear of them for so long. I had to admit that in town I could survive just fine by myself but up here in the mountains reality was I might need some help. Maybe that was the way God intended it to be. The guilt was really hitting me hard. I should've never doubted the man who had helped me reach safety in the first place. Now I would have to wait for his return to thank him. I decided to ponder things over down by the pond. I sat with my back against one of the large pine trees. What if my sister wasn't here? I was sure that every woman must have a man to help with things around the cabin like mending the fence or repairing the roof. Wood also needed to be chopped and fresh milk needed to be retrieved daily. Not to mention, someone would have to hunt the game up in the mountains. If I left Matthew would I survive the winter alone?

One hour and a half must have passed when Matthew sat himself down beside me on a rock. He had approached with such soft footsteps that I was surprised to see him. "I'm sorry you're angry Gracelyn. I figured you'd know where I was. You were so upset about your money I had to retrieve it. And, we'll need it before we leave this place." Matthew said. Suddenly, I felt very much alive and happy. It was kind of him to do that for me and he was right, we would need money before we were able to leave. It had only been a few days but I had already invested a lot into our little cabin. I'd baked, scrubbed the floors, cleaned the window panes of the film of dust they were covered in and even picked the last of the fall flowers which I'd made into a fresh bouquet for the table and hung the rest upside down to dry on the back porch. I was even fond of the back porch. It had a shelf to put extra water on and a sink to wash up in which Matthew did each time he came home. Home, I thought. It was my home now and I was beginning to love it. The truth was I had really missed Matthew. He was so polite and helpful. I couldn't leave him here all alone. I didn't want to. All of the sudden I realized I was afraid to be without him. I didn't understand what had happened these past few days and now it seemed I needed this man as I have no other in my life.

That night I continued to contemplate. There was much to be done around the settlement. The men would have to work from sun up til sun down to prepare for winter. The second round of the meadow grass would have to be cut for the animals. The animals needed to be strong and healthy if we were to survive winter. I knew that Matthew and I would be together no matter what the outcome would be. I had most of the money and Matthew had very little. This weighed on my conscious. I tiptoed into his room. The little bag of money was in my hand. I gently placed it on the pillow next to his head and tiptoed back to my room knowing I'd done the right thing. He would manage the money better than I and it would relieve any worry on his part. Yes, I could feel it in my heart, it was the right thing to do. I slept soundly that night knowing he was home. So soundly, in fact, when I awoke he was already gone for the day.

The men of the settlement worked hard resting only on Sabbath. They worked long hours each day preparing the third storage building. Supplies were brought in a wagon pulled by four horses. The men took turns going down the mountains to retrieve what they could. Matthew had been home for three weeks when it was his turn. I didn't want him to go. I tried to be brave as he reassured me but fear gripped me just as it had before. I ate little that day. As night fell, still no Matthew. I was perched in the rocking chair by the window. I couldn't sleep. I watched the moon move through the dark sky and then the sun rise which was beautiful. It wasn't cold enough for fires in the fireplace so I restocked the wood in the stove. I opened the front door and walked out onto the porch. There were no wagons approaching. Matthew was overdue and I was worried sick. I had just turned back toward the cabin when I heard the wagon wheels. I sighed with relief and thanked God for all of the men's safe return. I knew they would have to unload before Matthew would come home but at least he was here.

I was happy for the most part. I still didn't know what had happened to my sister. I asked Matthew for the thousandth time if there was any news about her that night. He replied, "No, you are still the only one in the settlement with red hair." "Red hair," I repeated, "Matthew, my sister doesn't look anything like me. She has short black hair and is thinner and taller than I am." He was silent for a moment and then he shot out of his chair and said, "Would your sister be Evee?" "Yes, yes yes!," I replied, "Not Evee, Ev, short for Evelyn. Where is she Matthew? Where is she?" Matthew was laughing as he slapped his long leg and told me to get a jacket on. He said we were going to visit.

We crossed over another bridge and walked around the edge of the mountain. A large patch of forest trees had been removed as well as the underbrush and the path was paved with small rocks. These men really worked hard and when they built something they did the job right the first time I thought. Before we had walked even half a mile from our cabin I heard the dogs barking. My dogs! I recognized their barks immediately. They must have followed my sister up the mountain when they couldn't find me. My sister looked just as surprised as I was when she opened the door. It was quite the reunion for all of us! My knees gave way to the floor, Cyndi jumped into my lap and Fluffy raced around barking as he always did when he became excited. I introduced Matthew to my family. He made small talk for a few minutes, making sure Ev was settled in and had someone caring for her needs. He said he would return in an hour to help me and the dogs home. My sister and I had so much to share. We began with our journey up the mountain. She had rode up in a wagon filled with children and the elderly. I sat there with my mouth open. Talk about the fickle finger of fate! I had worried myself sick over her and she'd spent the whole journey in a wagon! I was grateful though, if she had been in the wagon so had my little dogs. I had always been the stronger, more determined one. If one of us had to walk it was better me than her. I was more prepared. Ironic that she'd always told her friends I could've been one of the women who walked their way to the wild west in the early days. True to his word, Matthew returned an hour later. There was another older man with him. Matthew was such a good person. He always went out of his way to help others in need. I knew I was lucky.

It felt so good to sit in front of the fireplace with Fluffy in my lap and Cyndi at Matthew's side. For Cyndi, it was love at first site of Matthew and I could tell Matthew was fond of her too. God was good and I was grateful. Whatever I had lost didn't matter now. I had the important things, my sister, my dogs and Matthew, an unexpected surprise. I was too excited too sleep. The moon was full and it's silver rays shone into my bedroom. The dogs had taken their normal places, Cyndi at my feet and Fluffy snuggled as close to my side as he could get.

Soon winter would be upon us. Fall had come and was nearly gone. The beauty of the fall was etched in my mind. The beauty of the mountains that time of year is extraordinary. The men had worked long hours tending to anything that needed repair and cutting as much wood as they could. We all knew the snow could get as deep as six feet and that everything must be done before the first snowfall blanketed the ground. The wagons would be unable to pass anything deeper than four feet which made another trip down the mountain necessary for Matthew. It was his turn to drive. They would take five wagons in all. It would be the last trip until spring. Everything that was needed for winter must be retrieved now. Even when spring arrived travel could be delayed by the runoff of water from the melting snow.

Matthew returned safely in the afternoon. Upon his arrival home he placed a bundle in my lap. Surprised I asked, "What's this?" He grinned at me, which he seldom did, and replied, "Open it!" I did and once I unbound the bundle the most beautiful creme lace material slipped to the floor. I could see there were several yards, more than enough to cover all of our windows and then share some with my sister. She'd seemed a little sad the past few weeks and I hoped having a project would brighten her spirits. She was never fond of winter. I felt for her but knew we were both lucky we were near each other and that I'd just have to cheer her up these next few months. We were alive and safe and I'd constantly remind her of that.

I sewed endlessly, it seemed, until all of my windows were covered. They were lovely and I especially liked them when I could see and hear the rain falling outside. It was the perfect touch for our little cabin. It was amazing to think about how all of us had rallied together during our darkest days to create such a special settlement. We were so lucky up here. Sometimes, I would hear the men speak in low tones about the happenings below us. It was nothing they wanted the women to concern themselves with and that was probably for the best. I did wonder how much longer it would be before the large log gates would be closed and how well we would survive the winter. I would have my answers soon enough.

During the winter, Matthew and I visited my sister and Charlie often. Charlie had moved into my sister's empty bedroom at least for the winter to help with things like keeping the wood stocked. The white milk cows and the horses stayed warm in a large barn which was divided into two sections. The young men of the settlement tended to the horses. Everything that could be recycled in this settlement was. The waste from the animals was shoveled outside in large piles to be used in the spring for gardens. The center of the settlement was three miles from our cabin so I'd decided to shovel up the earth and create my own. We would have more than enough vegetables to share with my sister. The church which sat on a bit of a hill and faced the settlement was completed with a new bell. On Sundays, the bell was heard throughout the settlement and we all gathered with our different faiths to worship. It no longer mattered what religion you practiced as we all believed in the same God. For Matthew and I the winter months passed quickly. Not much had changed besides Cyndi now slept on Matthew's bed. There was nothing romantic between us. We were just two lucky people thrown together, trying to do our best, just as everyone else was. I personally loved the mountains in all of the seasons. I loved my home and was grateful my sister lived nearby. Life moved at a slower pace now and in ways was much more simple.

The women gathered in the spring in the new town hall to begin preparing for next winter. There were old fashioned quilting frames and when we met we would sew. This turned into hours of good talk with friends. We shared wedding news, baby stories and the normal gossip of friends. The roads were still impassable but the snow pack was slowly melting off. Some flowers had even sprung up in the areas which had been sheltered from the snow. By the third spring my garden was dug, surrounded by a white picket fence, and did quite well. There were baskets of flowers hanging on the porch which we had roofed the previous fall. The back porch was screened and in the summers we ate all of our meals on it. It was so secluded with sounds of water falling and such beautiful scenery, definitely one of my favorite places. The wagons went down the mountain more frequently now. Times had become more dangerous. Last fall, a guardsman raced his horse through town crying for help to shut the gates. Our settlement was designed to be self sufficient so of course unwelcome people tried to get in to help themselves to our supplies, food and more. A house now stood at the gates for guardsmen to take turns living in. It was sad to see how the times were slowly changing but good times were still had. The Fourth of July was a big summer celebration. We all prepared our favorite dishes and gathered for an afternoon of fun.

I wasn't sure what had gotten into Matthew. He seemed to follow me where ever I went these days. One day I was tired of him following me, and angry that he was hot on my trail to my sister's house. I'd had enough. I stormed around and stomped back to our cabin, slamming the door in his face. That was the last time he followed me to Ev's house but he still came to town with me.

The following summer something strange happened. I was on my way to Ev's when I heard voices on the other side of the boulder. I could identify Matthew's voice but not the other man. I knew it was wrong but I crept back to listen. "Have you told Gracelyn? She needs to prepare herself for the journey," the stranger said. Matthew replied, "She's not going to like it. She loves it here and actually, so do I." The stranger had the voice of an old man and he was becoming stern. "It's time. It can no longer be delayed. Both of you must come back and she needs to marry and assume her role as a high priestess.", he said. I heard Matthew snap back, "She doesn't love him! When he sat beside her bed in town he was actually rude to her. Santiago doesn't love her either. This is wrong and she should not marry that arrogant man." I was the center of this discussion and decided I had every right to peek around the corner to see who this older man was. I was so surprised when I saw his attire that I let out a loud gasp. Both men heard me and turned to see who had discovered them. I ran as fast as my legs would carry me to my sister's house. My head was spinning with questions like who was that old man and what did he want with me. He wore a long purple robe and a hat on top of his head. He had a long white mustache and beard. It occurred to me then that I had seen men dressed like him before. Before I made the journey up the mountain, in my old bedroom. At first I was visited by white doves, just a few for several years and then more appeared. I felt they had been sent from above to guard me. And then, a man had appeared. He had come to heal my aching legs. I had been having trouble with circulation and swelling for a long time. As time went on, more men dressed similarly to the man I had just seen with Matthew appeared. What did this man mean when he said I needed to prepare myself? And Matthew was certainly right when he said I didn't love Santiago. Santiago is indeed an arrogant man, thirty years younger than me and a small framed man. I was not really attracted to smaller men and had no memory of Santiago from a former life nor could I picture myself creating memories with him in this lifetime. There was something about him I just didn't like.

By now, I was too stunned and upset to go to my sister's home. She would immediately know something was wrong. So, instead I walked three miles into town. When I arrived at the church the afternoon sun gleamed through the stained glass windows. I sat on the church bench until dusk. If I didn't leave now I would have to make my way home in the pitch black darkness of night. It was dangerous to walk at night because of the numerous bridges. We used torches to light the way but over the years people had missed the bridge and fallen into the river.

Through the front window of our cabin I saw Matthew pacing back and forth. I always knew when Matthew was upset because he ran his fingers through his long hair. He was doing that now and I knew something was very wrong. When I opened the door Matthew said, "Where were you? Didn't you think about how worried I would be when you ran off and were nowhere to be found? From now on, you tell me exactly where you're going and when." Well, I thought, he has no right to talk to me in that tone. I walked past him and slammed my bedroom door in his face as hard as I could. I sat down on my bed fuming and listened to Matthew pounding on the door. "You open this door Gracelyn or I swear I'll break it down. We have to talk about this now." I wasn't the one who had snuck off into the woods to have conversations about him with a weird man and I wasn't going to talk to him about it now. I knew I wasn't going to get a peaceful bath tonight and figured I might as well just undress and crawl into bed now. I despised going to bed unbathed and knew I wouldn't sleep well but I probably wouldn't sleep well anyway. I heard a loud thud at my door. I had locked Matthew out and he must've blocked the doorway. Was he so dense he didn't think I would just crawl out the window? At midnight I tried to open the door but I wasn't strong enough to push it open. I waited until I thought Matthew had gone to bed before I opened the window and removed the screen. I boosted myself up into the frame and turned myself around. Why wasn't I taller? Most people would be able to touch the ground but there I was with my feet dangling in the air. I let go and landed on my bottom. I was lucky to not hit my head. There in the dark I heard, "Well, what took you so long Gracelyn? I've been waiting out here since Midnight. How about we strike a truce? Don't run away and I'll tell you what is happening."

I sat inside and watched as Matthew stocked the fire in the stove and prepared the coffee pot. He sat down, waiting for the water to boil. "Hear me out before you start asking questions please." Matthew said as he poured each of us a cup of coffee. He made a gesture toward our rockers with his head and handed me my cup. There was still a small fire burning and rocking next to it calmed my nerves a bit. "The world has five planes Gracelyn. You and I exist on the highest plane below God. We live and work, marry and even bear children. On this plane some are wealthy some are poor. Some work hard and some are losing ground because of their greed. But, in the way you knew life before you are actually dead Gracelyn. On this plane, Gracelyn, you are considered a priestess, a high priestess held with much regard. And well, to put it bluntly, you are a very wealthy woman, you have a large dowry. This dowery has always been there waiting for you. Gracelyn, haven't you wondered why the stars and the moon dance in the sky for you?" I was dazed. Since I can remember the full moon brings creatures of all sorts to me like birds, owls and chipmunks. "How did you know about that? Do you know my great grandmother? Her name was LaDuc." I asked. He replied, "Yes, I know her but not as well as Santiago." I stopped him there. I wasn't sure what to make of the entire situation, of my own existence and I didn't want to hear anymore. "I can't handle anything else Matthew, I need to go to bed." I got up, returned to my bedroom and crawled beneath the sheets.

From that morning on, these men, dressed in robes, were always with me when I left the cabin. The only retrieve I had was in the cabin with Matthew. I was never alone and I hated it. I could feel their presence as soon as I opened the door. I began losing weight, I felt like a prisoner. Over the weeks rumors began that they were rebuilding the city. The worst was over people said. I had become so accustomed to living in the mountains that my city life seemed as if it were a thousand years ago. I wondered what kind of life I would be left with. I certainly did not want to marry Santiago as the old man had told Matthew. Things were happening though, things I couldn't ignore. I had visions of a boy, a boy who was my son and his father was Santiago. My son wanted me to remarry his father. There were doves everywhere. Matthew said that it was Santiago's way of guiding me home safely. Home, I thought, my home is here. My heart cried everyday. I was so happy here with Matthew, why must it end? And my sister, who would watch over here if I was gone?

One day I decided I needed answers and Matthew was the only one that seemed to have them. "Matthew," I said, "I don't love Santiago. I have glimpses of the past. He hasn't changed. He was cold then and he'll be even colder this time. My age makes a tremendous difference now." Matthew put his finger to his mouth to silence me. He said, "You must marry him. It is for the better of all people. Your dowry will help others, it will help families Gracelyn. They need you and we are leaving in three days. You need to say your goodbyes."

He hated this. He hated encouraging Gracelyn to remarry Santiago. He had always loved her and he loved her now. Matthew felt sick. He knew he was doing what he must do. Matthew silently hoped Gracelyn would refuse Santiago in the end. Gracelyn had a choice. Even if she didn't marry Santiago her son would be cared for and well taken care of. It was God's will that she make the final decision for herself and Matthew knew he couldn't interfere.

Our final morning came. Matthew advised me to dress in a wool dress to avoid a chill during our trip. I said goodbye to my sister and she stood on the porch sobbing. I had my dog Fluffy in one arm and I slowly shut the door. Matthew had Cyndi. They had been waiting by something that looked like a hot air balloon. We got in. I looked up and saw my doves, ten of them. They appeared much larger now though. Each had a string in their beak and we ascended into the sky. I was in awe of the entire situation and even more shocked when I saw my sister's first husband, who had been dead for years, in the meadow. My sister saw him too. They hugged and kissed and I knew she would enjoy the rest of her time. At least this had a happy ending for her I thought. I realized that everyone was free to leave safely. It appeared only three families chose to leave the settlement. I understood why everyone else stayed. I would have loved to stay there myself with Matthew.

The dogs and I awoke when we landed. I didn't remember the upward voyage or falling asleep. Both dogs immediately began barking but Matthew quickly calmed them. The land was different here. There was a lot of soft sand. There was a wide river which ran past a beautiful salmon colored mansion. There were balconies on both levels which overlooked the surrounding rose gardens and numerous fountains. Matthew led me down a small walkway and into a gazebo. It was a big gazebo covered with trellis. The only opening led to different paths, one led to the house. Had this been my home in the past. I was overwhelmed with emotions. It was beautiful though. Someone had set a table for three and prepared refreshments. My stomach fluttered and I could not eat a thing but I did accept a drink.

It was delicious, some sort of sweet fruit I thought. Matthew had left me alone. I wished he was here now though because I didn't want to encounter Santiago by myself. I glanced at a woman who appeared to be the maid when I heard footsteps on the path. She blushed and I rose out of my chair. I shuttered at the thought of facing my former and future husband. I saw Santiago walking toward me on the stone pathway. He was well groomed and dressed in a long sleeved white silk shirt with black satin pants and a belt around his slender waist. He appeared so young in comparison to me. I had seen him before in my bedroom in the city. I awoke one night to find him watching me sleep. I had chills then and again now. He looked the same as he had then. After a formal introduction he said, "Why aren't you properly dressed?" Although I wasn't sure why, I could feel a blush come over my face. "As of yet, I've had no place to do so." "Oh so sorry," Santiago said, "I assumed you'd remember your quarters. This is your home Gracelyn." He turned the maid and said, "Girl fetch your Mistress' maids and bring them to her at once. She needs a bath." I was insulted. I bathed at least once a day for as long as I could remember. Before I could bring forth an insult to match his own, he was gone.

As the day wore on, things became more familiar. I did remember my quarters but I was unsure of the balcony. It was beautiful with marble steps which led back down to the garden paths. The paths led to the river which was approximately a half mile from the house. There was a large boathouse on the river and I wasn't surprised to see it full of boats. The boats had brought guests. The guests were here for the formal dinner which had been planned before my arrival. The dinner was to announce my forthcoming marriage.

The maids arrived promptly at seven that evening. They groomed and began to dress me. A beautiful white silk gown was strewn across the bed. I looked in my closet and removed a red dress. The dress was made of yards of material which would wrap around me. It had a round collar, sleeves just past the elbow and just barely touched the floor. The maids frowned but said nothing. I wondered if someone would be coming for me when I heard a knock on the door. One of the maids opened it and there was Matthew. He stood in the doorway looking as handsome as ever. Tears welled up in my eyes. I ran to him and through my arms around his neck. "Please Matthew, please take us home." I cried. I felt his arms tighten around my waist. He whispered softly, "We have an audience. The maids are watching. I wish with all of my heart that it was possible to return but it would not be permitted." I looked up into his eyes. It was the first time I'd ever seen his tears. It was at that moment I knew he loved me as I loved him. I whispered back, "Am I permitted to choose my husband? Do I have the right to choose no matter who it is?" "Gracelyn," Matthew said, "You are a priestess. No one could refuse you and live to tell about it. Not even me." In a hushed tone I thanked him and told him that was all I needed to know. The maids had fled and I knew it was time to go downstairs. Matthew whispered one last thing to me. He told me he was happy I wore the red dress, that I looked beautiful in it.

The dining hall was packed with all sorts of people waiting for my entrance. Matthew led me to the head table where Santiago stood behind his chair. Matthew turned and headed toward a table full of young and old men. I looked to the left and saw another table. It was longer than the one Matthew sat at and was full of couples. I could tell they were whispering back and forth to each other. I stood behind my chair and once again, blushed. My face was the same shade as my long gown. The men, including Matthew, bowed to me. I wondered what was going on. Santiago said curtly no one can be seated until you are. "Oh, I'm sorry," I said, "I didn't know." Santiago replied, "I see there's much to teach you in the skills of being a lady as well as a wife." Silently I replied, "Santiago, you have nothing to worry about." A harp positioned on a small platform played while we dined. The music was hauntingly beautiful. I forced myself to nibble on the bread and some of the fruit. Finally, I gave up on eating, drank the wine and watched the others enjoy what appeared to be quite the meal. My eyes met with Matthew's several times but he quickly looked away. Santiago must have noticed. He leaned over to me and said, "My dear, once we are married you must be more discreet." The words flew out of my mouth. "Like you Santo? Where is your dark haired mistress this evening? Does she lay waiting for you to knock on her door?" I was embarrassed but it was too late now. The wine on my empty stomach had loosened my tongue. I could see I'd ruffled his feathers. "When we are married and matters are in my hands I have a lot to say to you." he responded. "I couldn't agree more Santo. I would certainly have a lot to say as well."

Santiago led me to another table. I wasn't sure why I hadn't noticed it before. It was placed on a platform and seated around it were the men dressed in long purple robes and hats that matched. These were the men I'd seen in my bedroom, with Matthew and who had been with me during my last weeks in the mountains. Santiago bowed in front of them and then turned to me. I heard him say choose me Gracelyn. After all I was your husband before and we have a son. The maids hurried forward and wrapped a white gown around me. I realized then why Matthew was so happy to see me in red. I'd chosen the wrong gown for the special occasion. A high backed chair was brought forward and placed in front of me. Trumpets began to play. I quickly sat down. The bachelors had formed a single file line and waited for their chance to approach me. I couldn't believe what was happening. My God, I thought, they came in all different shapes, sizes and age. I barely noticed any of them though and then Matthew approached. My heart stood still. A row of men formed in front of me. I looked at each one and shook my head no until only Matthew and Santiago were left. At last, this most humiliating ordeal was almost over. I looked from one to the other. The closer I looked the more I could see similarities in their features. I wondered if they were kin. Santiago's face was turning red and I could tell he was furious. "Enough," he said, "Choose!" "Very well Santiago. I have chosen." Santiago stepped forward and then stopped dead in his tracks when I asked Matthew to come to me. We wrapped our hands together tightly and stepped over to what I realized was the table of Priests. I could hear a great deal of gasping and whispers that weren't so quiet behind us.

"I, as high Priestess, have chosen my husband. Let the vows be spoken. For I take Matthew as my husband for all my life and the lives which may yet come." I said with clarity and confidence. I knew everyone including the Priests were in awe but I didn't care. One of the Priests said, "But your son!" I replied, "Yes I know of my son. I plan to take care of him financially and Matthew and I will welcome him into our lives. He may always call our home his for as long as he likes. After all, we are family and I am his mother. I will always be available for my son."

After the vows were complete the older Priest signed papers. These papers made my dowry Matthew's. He was a wealthy man now. Santiago was no where to be found. The music played as rows of people began congratulating us. A young dark and very handsome man approached me. He held his hand out for mine and said, "May your life be happier than it was before mother." Then he turned toward Matthew and said, "If anyone but my father was to marry my mother I am glad it is you. We are family." Finally seeing my son was an exciting experience. Almost comparable to a pregnant mother anxiously awaiting the birth of her baby. But, I was exhausted. "Matthew, I'm exhausted. Can we retire for the evening?" Matthew replied with a smile, "Certainly. Where would you like to spend our first night together?" "I'd like to say our cabin but now that I've met my son I can't leave him." I said. "I know the perfect place but you'll have to change into something else." Matthew said. "And where will you be waiting for me?" I asked. "Sitting there watching you." He replied. Shocked I blurted out, "Oh no!" Matthew said, "Oh yes! "The dogs Matthew, where are they?" I asked. "I took the liberty of taking them to my house this morning," he replied.

We walked from my quarters, onto the balcony and down the lighted path. When we arrived at the boat house a canoe was waiting! The canoe had a canopy and cushions for seating. A young boy took the paddles and we headed down stream. It wasn't long before we anchored and stepped ashore. Matthew whispered in my ear, "You're mine, all mine and you're home Gracelyn. Home!" I looked over and saw a lawn covered in flowers. The garden and the house were lit up as if someone was expected. I looked at Matthew and asked "Were you expecting a party?" "No", he said, "I just knew I'd need all the light I could get for if need be I'd have stole you away from Santiago. Rightfully, you've always belonged to me. You see Santiago erased my name, replaced it with his and married you. Before I could present solid proof, you were with child. My son, yes, he should have been my son Gracelyn, yours and mine. The eldest Priest knew the truth and that's why little was said during the wedding. Well, we're home, not fancy like the one you just left but" I interrupted with, "Thank God for that! I hate great big houses!" Matthew said, "Gracelyn, that house is yours. Santiago has been living in it." "With your permission, I'd like to sign it over to my son and Santiago." I said. Matthew nodded yes. "Matthew," I asked, "Are you related to Santiago? I just feel it. What relation is he to you?" "I am his brother." Matthew replied. "Than it's your job to help him, within reason." I said "I hope he marries the dark haired woman. He's crazy about her." "Does anything get past you?" Matthew asked. "You almost did and I'm here to tell you you're mine at last. You're mine and I'm never letting you go. Finally we're home Matthew. We're finally home!"

The End